Zillions of Practice Problems
for
Beginning Algebra

Zillions of Practice Problems
for
Beginning Algebra

Stanley F. Schmidt, Ph.D.

Polka Dot Publishing

ISBN: 978-1-937032-04-3

Printed and bound in the United States of America

Polka Dot Publishing   Reno, Nevada

To order copies of books in the Life of Fred series,

visit our website PolkaDotPublishing.com

Questions or comments? Email the author at lifeoffred@yahoo.com

Fifth printing

Zillions of Practice Problems for Beginning Algebra was illustrated by the author with additional clip art furnished under license from Nova Development Corporation, which holds the copyright to that art.

for Goodness' sake

or as J.S. Bach—who was
never noted for his plain
English—often expressed it:

Ad Majorem Dei Gloriam
(to the greater glory of God)

If you happen to spot an error that the author, the publisher, and the printer missed, please let us know with an email to: lifeoffred@yahoo.com

As a reward, we'll email back to you a list of all the corrections that readers have reported for this book.

What This Book Is All About

In the *Life of Fred: Beginning Algebra Expanded Edition* book, there are *Your Turn to Play* sections after each topic is presented. And each *Your Turn to Play* offers complete solutions to each question.

At the end of each chapter are three problem sets, each named after a city. Each of the problems in these cities is also completely worked out in the book.

I thought that all those problems would be enough.
I still think all those problems are enough.
As they say in German: *Genug ist genug.*[*]

❀   ❀   ❀

Some of my readers have written to me, "Enough is not enough. We want more. We want tons of problems along with completely worked out solutions. We need the drill-and-kill approach. My kids are not crying when they read Fred—how could they be learning math without crying?"

If you are a part of those *some readers*, then this *Zillions of Practice Problems* was written for you.

HOW THIS BOOK IS ORGANIZED

Life of Fred: Beginning Algebra Expanded Edition is in twelve chapters. This book also has twelve chapters.

As you work through each chapter in *Life of Fred: Beginning Algebra Expanded Edition*, you can do as many of the problems as you like in the corresponding chapter in this book.

---

[*] "Enough is enough." I learned this nifty phrase when I studied German in high school.

CHAPTERS IN THIS BOOK

Each chapter in this book is divided into two parts.

★ The first part takes each topic and offers a zillion problems.

★ The second part is called the 𝕸ixed 𝕭ag. It consists of a variety of problems from the chapter and review problems from the beginning of the book up to that point.

COMPLETE SOLUTIONS

Every problem (gasp!) will receive a detailed solution—not just the answer.

ELIMINATING TEMPTATION

The solutions and answers are all given in the back half of the book. The first question in this book is numbered "45." The second one is "888." In most ordinary practice books, they are numbered, "1, 2, 3 . . ." which is really silly when you think about it. In those books, when you look up the answer to "1" you might accidentally see the answer to "2" and that would spoil all the fun.

Contents

First part: Problems on Each Topic

Sets

45. Using braces, give an example of a set with two elements in it.

888. Are these sets equal? {A, ✪} and {✪, A}

500. If two sets are equal, must they have the same number of elements?

317. Why is it is incorrect to write {7} + 6?

923. Using braces, list the set of all people who have eight eyes.

71. If set C has three elements in it, and set D has four elements in it, can these two sets be equal?

221. Using braces give an example of a set that contains four members, exactly one of which is the first name of a former President of the United States.

699. List the set that contains a right bracket and a left parenthesis.

900. List a set that contains exactly 88 elements.

Finite and Infinite Sets

123. Is the set of all words in the English language finite or infinite?

635. Is the set of all the grains of sand on all the beaches in the world finite or infinite?

405. Is the set of natural numbers {1, 2, 3, . . . } finite or infinite?

37. Is the number of elements in the empty set finite or infinite ?

560. Could the government print an infinite number of dollar bills?

492. Using braces, give four examples of infinite sets.

Natural Numbers, Whole Numbers, Integers

838. Using braces, list the whole numbers.

187. Explain why this set of whole numbers is not equal to the set of natural numbers.

589. Is 5.7 a natural number?

200. Name a natural number that is not an integer, if possible.
347. Name the smallest possible whole number.
518. Name the smallest possible integer.
726. Name the largest negative integer.

Adding Integers

714. $30 + (-10)$
855. $7 + (-4)$
944. $15 + (-20)$
977. $100 + (-5)$
986. $-17 + (+7)$
640. $-40 + 8$
616. $-7 + (-8)$
460. $-19 + 39$
333. $(+20) + (-7) + (+5) + (-4)$
240. $(-8) + (-8) + (-8) + 3$
188. $52 + (-13) + 10 + (-13)$

Subtracting Integers

655. $8 - (+5)$
742. $14 - (-3)$
913. $500 - (-800)$
959. $-3 - (-12)$
989. $-70 - (-30)$
521. $99 - (-70)$
356. $-22 - (-3)$
585. $30 - (+40)$
682. $1000 - (-25)$
729. $66 - (+88)$
866. $10 + (-11) - (-40)$
925. $-6 - (+28) - (-9) + (-2) + (+7)$
891. $15 - (-17) - (+3)$
840. $8 - 500$ This is the same as $8 - (+500)$

Going from 4 to 11

445. Going from 4 to 11 means . . .

494. Going from 38 to 32 means . . .

864. Going from –5 to +5 means . . .

685. If we go from –7° to +40°, how much did the temperature climb?

593. If we go from 55° down to –8°, how much did the temperature change?

732. If your net worth was –$500 in January and it was $800 in March, how much did you gain?

917. If my checking account was overdrawn by $70 and after making a deposit it was $800, how much was the deposit?

980. Before the storm, my house was worth a million dollars. After the storm it was worth $100,000. How much did the value of my house change?

532. If I start at the top of Mt. Everest (29,028 feet above sea level) and walk down to the ocean and then dive 30 feet under the sea, how much have I changed my elevation?

Ratio

619. For every soda you buy, you get three straws. What is the ratio of sodas to straws?

718. For every soda you buy, you get three straws. What is the ratio of straws to sodas?

852. For every four pepperoni pizzas that PieOne sells, it sells three combination pizzas. What is the ratio of pepperoni pizzas to combination pizzas?

39. It takes three hours for every two pages of Life of Fred that I write. What is the ratio of hours to pages?

154. Express 7/33 as a ratio.

326. Express 9 ÷ 5 as a ratio.

467. If I measure the time it takes me to grow my sunflowers in days and then measure that in weeks, what is the ratio of those two measurements?

511. If I measure the length of my driveway in yards and then measure it in feet, what is the ratio of those two measurements?

Second part: the 𝕄ixed 𝔹ag: a variety of problems from this chapter and possibly previous material

207. If I went on the number line from 6 to –5, by how much did my position change?

441. –600 + 200

540. Name an integer that is not a whole number.

624. Using braces, give an example of an infinite set that contains the planet Neptune.

667. Using braces, list the set of movie stars who ate 18 pounds of spaghetti for breakfast yesterday.

845. If oil costs $121 a barrel, what is the ratio of barrels to dollars?

907. $18 - (-20) - (+7) + (-3)$

2930. For every 157 miles I jog, I lose 3 pounds. What is the ratio of miles to pounds?

1690. Express $\frac{2}{3}$ as a ratio.

1706. If you owed someone $33 and that person both forgave the debt and gave you $44, how much richer would you be?

930. What are "{" and "}" called?

651. My daily gains and losses in the stock market for one week were: +48, –60, –3, –8, and +17. What was the total change for the week?

401. If set A is the set of all integers less than 5 and set B is the set of all whole numbers less than 5, does set A equal set B?

2222. The cardinality of a set is the number of elements in that set. For example, the cardinality of {Й, Ж, Б} is 3. The cardinality of { } is zero. The whole numbers are often used to describe the cardinality of a set. Give an example of set whose cardinality is *not* a whole number.

3000. What is the cardinality of {⅔}?

1277. 2^5 is equal to what natural number?

1889. Fill in the blank: $-5 + \underline{\ ?\ } = 15$

1313. $-22 - 7$

1585. If I went on the number line from –7 to –5, by how much did my position change?

Chapter Two

First part: Problems on Each Topic

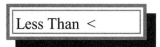

Less Than <

1600. Is it true that –400 < –4?

2275. Fill in the blank with an integer that will make this true: __?__ < –14.

3333. Which of these are true?

$$\frac{1}{2} < \frac{1}{4} \qquad -\frac{1}{3} < -\frac{1}{6} \qquad -55 < 3 \qquad -0.01 < -0.1$$

5585. > means "greater than." Complete this sentence:

x > z if and only if z . . .

1717. ≥ means "greater than or equal to." Which of these are true?

$$444 \geq 444 \qquad 0.1 \geq 0.01 \qquad -6 \geq -98 \qquad 5\frac{1}{3} \geq -100$$

960. Make a guess what ≤ means.

1362. Complete this sentence: w ≥ y iff y . . .

"iff" means "if and only if"

1921. = means "equal to."

≠ means "is not equal to."

∈ means "is an element of." For example, **3** ∈ {A, #, **3**}.

Make a guess what ∉ means.

1663. Is it possible to find a number x, such that x < x?

2270. Is it possible to find a number y, such that y ≤ y?

Multiplying and Dividing Integers

3116. Using braces, list the integers.

4444. If you multiply two integers together, the rule is:

Signs alike ⇨ Answer is positive.

Signs different ⇨ Answer is negative.

What is the rule for dividing two integers?

6121. (+8)(–7)

(–9)(–6)

(10)(–10)

3256. When you multiply three numbers together, you first multiply two of them, and then you multiply that answer by the third number. You can't multiply all three numbers together at the same time.

For example, (3)(4)(6)

= 12(6)

= 72

Multiply together (−5)(+2)(−7).

1001. −56/−7

1409. If you multiply together four negative numbers, what will the sign of the answer be?

1748. If we multiply eight negative numbers together, what will the sign of the answer be?

1111. If we multiply 1,000,001 negative numbers together, what will be the sign of the answer?

1371. Fill in the two blanks:

If you multiply together an even number of negative numbers, the answer will always be ___?___ .

If you multiply together an odd number of negative numbers, the answer will always be ___?___ .

1625. Suppose that you multiply together 81 integers. Suppose that 40 of them are positive, 40 are negative and one of them is zero. Describe the answer that you will get.

1830. If you multiply together 40 different integers, and 21 of them are positive and the rest are negative, what will be the sign of the answer?

Proportions

1926. Fill in the blank: A proportion is the equality of two ___?___ .

2284. If $7 will buy 3 pizzas, how many pizzas will $56 buy?

3160. Joe bought 3 cupcakes for $14. How many could he buy for $140?

Pi π

2291. Draw a picture of a circle. Then draw its diameter.

2249. Will the diameter of a circle always pass through the center of the circle?

3299. π is approximately equal to 3.14159265358979.

   Is π < 3.1416?

4004. $\frac{22}{7}$ ≈ 3.142857142857142857142857142857. (Notice how this decimal repeats itself every six digits.)

≈ means "approximately equal to."

   Is π < $\frac{22}{7}$?

4811. Suppose a pizza had a diameter of 7 feet. What would be its *exact* circumference?

6204. Suppose a pizza had a diameter of 7 feet and using $\frac{22}{7}$ for π, what would be the circumference of this pizza?

2289. If π is approximately equal to 3.14159265358979, what would 1000π be approximately equal to?

2255. Every fraction (of an integer divided by an integer) can be expressed as a repeating decimal.

For example: $\frac{1}{2}$ = 0.50000000000000000000000000 . . .

   $\frac{1}{3}$ = 0.33333333333333333333333333 . . .

   $\frac{1}{6}$ = 0.83333333333333333333333333 . . .

   $\frac{1}{7}$ = 0.142857142857142857142857142857 . . .

Expressing π as a decimal yields a non-repeating decimal. π ≈

3.14159265358979323846264338327950288419716939937510582097494459230781640628620899862803482534211706798214808651328230664709384460955058223172535940812848111745028410270193852110555964462294895493038192644288109756659334461284756482337867831652712019091456485669234603486104543266482133936072602491412737245870066063155881748815209209628292540917153436789259036001133053054882046652138414695194151160943305727036575959195309218611738193261179310511854807446237996274956735188575272489122793818301194912983367336244065664308602139494639522473719070217986094370277053921717629317675238467481846766940513200056812714526356082778577134275778960917363717872146844090122495343014654958537105079227968925892354201995611212902196086403441815981362977477130996051870721134999999983729780499510597317328160963185950244594553469083026425223082533446850352619311881710100031378387528865875332083814206171776691473035982534904287554687311595628638823537875937519577818577805321712268066130019278766111959092164201989380952572010654858632788659366

Can π be expressed as a fraction (of an integer divided by an integer)?

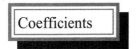

Coefficients

2898. What is the coefficient of 6xyz?

3302. What is the coefficient of 3.142857142857142857142857142d?

5700. What is the coefficient of $w^5x^2y^8$?

Second part: the 𝔐ixed 𝔅ag: a variety of problems from this chapter and previous material

2203. The product (multiplication) of two negative numbers is always positive. What can you say about the sum (addition) of two negative numbers?

1836. The product (multiplication) of a positive number and a negative number is always negative. What can you say about the sum (addition) of a positive number and a negative number?

2210. Name an integer that makes this true: $-5 >$ ___?___

3209. If you express 1000π as a decimal, is it a repeating or a non-repeating decimal?

4512. If you express 0π as a decimal is it a repeating or a non-repeating decimal?

5525. If I know that some number times -3987 equals a positive answer, what can I say about that number?

6181. $(-5)(+7)(-2)$

6711. If one slice of Stanthony's Finest Combo Pizza weighs 2.8 pounds, how much would 7 slices weigh?

8888. What is the cardinality of {7, 8, 9}?

7103.  A table is 56 inches across. What is the circumference of that table? Use $\frac{22}{7}$ for π.

5566. If a table has a diameter of 56", what is its radius?

4518. If 4 birdhouses cost $27, how much would 8 birdhouses cost?

4278. What is the coefficient of x^3y^{44}?

3325. Name a whole number x, such than x < 3.

9009. $(-6)(+9)$

      $(+8)(-8)(-10)$

      $(-2)(-2)(-2)(-2)(-2)$

4466. You buy a bunch of identical bird statues.

Name something that is proportional to the number of statues you bought.

5580. Filling in each blank with either $\in$ or $\notin$:

      5 __?__ $\{-2, -1, 0, 1, 2, \ldots, 40, 41, 42\}$

      7 __?__ the set of integers

      $\triangle$ __?__ $\{\circledast, \circledcirc, \vDash, \mathbb{I}\}$

6187. $(99.392)(\frac{1}{3})(\sqrt{311})(0)(-100)(0.33333333)$

8329. You and your friend, Roger, are on opposite sides of the earth. (If you were to dig a hole directly downwards, you would eventually see the bottom of Roger's feet. The earth has a diameter of about 8,000 miles.

    Instead of digging the hole, you walk/swim around the surface of the planet to see Roger. How far would you have to go? (Use 3 for π.)

9070. You multiply together ten numbers. Four of them are positive, and four of them are negative. What can you say about the answer?

8411. Which of these are true?

$$\frac{1}{2} \geq \frac{1}{2}$$

$$\frac{1}{4} \leq \frac{1}{8}$$

$$\frac{1}{5} > \frac{1}{6}$$

$$-\frac{1}{5} > -\frac{1}{6}$$

6300. $(-12)/(+3)$

      $(-54)/(-9)$

      $(36)/(-9)$

      $(10)/(-100)$

Chapter Three

First part: Problems on Each Topic

Equations with Continued Ratios

8912. In my garden, the roses, daisies, and marigolds are in the continued ratio 5:6:9. I have a total of 120 plants. How many daisies do I have?

7020. Among my 96 friends, for every 3 friends who like red as their favorite color, there are 7 who like blue, and 2 who like green. How many of these 96 friends like green as their favorite color?

6148. Joe likes to collect balls of gum. For every 5 cherry-flavored balls, he has 2 blueberry-flavored, 11 chocolate-flavored and 7 mint-flavored balls. He has a total of 625 gum balls in those four flavors. How many of each flavor does he have?

Geometry Formulas

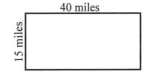

6222. Here is a piece of land in Texas.
What is its perimeter?
What is its area?

6411. If a rectangle has a width of 9 inches and an area of 108 square inches, what is its length?

7304. If a rectangle has a width of 5.4 yards and an area of 45.9 square yards, what is its length?

8950. A trapezoid is a four-sided figure in which exactly two sides are parallel. For any trapezoid, the area is equal to $A = \frac{1}{2} h(a + b)$ where h is the distance between the parallel lines, and a and b are the lengths of the parallel sides.

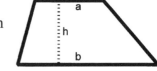

What is the area of a trapezoid where the lengths of the parallel sides are 9 and 15 feet, and the distance between the parallel sides is 7 feet?

9122. A trapezoid has an area of 980 square inches and the lengths of the parallel sides are 60 and 80 inches. What is the distance between the parallel sides?

Chapter Three

Consecutive Numbers

7777. What is the next consecutive number that comes after n?

6408. If n is the first of three consecutive *odd* numbers, what are the next two?

7041. If n is the last of four consecutive numbers, what are the first three?

8332. If n is the last of three consecutive *even* numbers, what are the first two?

8695. Name three consecutive numbers that add to 138.

6274. Find three consecutive even numbers that add to 2166.

9081. The weight of Fred, a large size Stanthony combo pizza, and Darlene's nail polish collection are three consecutive numbers (in that order), when weighed in pounds. If you put Fred, the pizza, and Darlene's nail polish collection on a scale, it would weigh 111 pounds. How much does the pizza weigh?

Set Builder Notation

6685. Express in English: { x | x is a movie star}.

7105. Write { x | x + 4 = 7} as a set without using set builder notation.

8895. Write { x | x times x equals 25} as a set without using set builder notation. Note that { x | x times x equals 25} could also have been expressed as { x | $x^2 = 25$}.

8973. Write { x | x = 2n where n is a natural number} as a set without using set builder notation.

7792. Using set builder notation, write the set {100, 101, 102, . . . , 996, 997, 998, 999}.

Reflexive Property of Equality
Symmetric Property of Equality
Distributive Property

6702. Why is it true that 5(x + w) = 5x + 5w?

20. Why is it true that $6x^2y + 55\xi = 6x^2y + 55\xi$?

204. If we know that $7\xi = \sqrt{5}$, by what reason can we say that $\sqrt{5} = 7\xi$?

351. If we know that $99x + 99y = 32$, by what reason can we say that $99(x + y) = 32$?

453. If we know that $5x = 37$, by what reason can we say that $37 = 5x$?

527. Fill in the reasons why each line follows from the previous line:

$$4(x + y) + 3x^6 = \pi d$$
$$4x + 4y + 3x^6 = \pi d \qquad \underline{\quad ? \quad}$$
$$\pi d = 4x + 4y + 3x^6 \qquad \underline{\quad ? \quad}$$

8898. $7(8x + 9y) = ?$

Rational Numbers

629. Using set builder notation, define the rational numbers.

711. Is every whole number a rational number?

790. Is every rational number a natural number?

1380. Some student might say that π is a rational number because it can be written as $\frac{\pi}{1}$. Why would that student be wrong?

Order of Operations

1630. $6 \cdot 8 + 60 / 10$

1844. $36 / 9 \cdot 4$

6730. $10 + 20 / 40$

8000. $8 \cdot 4 + 2$

8413. $12 / 6 \cdot 2$

Distance = (rate)(time) Problems

8870. The army van heads south from KITTENS University at 30 mph. Four hours later, Betty and Alexander head south from KITTENS University chasing the army van. They are going 50 mph. How long will it take Betty and Alexander to catch up with the army van? (Let t = the number of hours it will take them to catch up.)

8989. Do the previous problem using the "Six Pretty Boxes" approach that was taught in *Life of Fred: Pre-Algebra 2*. (If you somehow missed that approach, please just turn to the answer, and you can learn this alternative to the ① Let t = . . . ; ② Then . . . approach we used in the previous problem.

9303. Darlene and Joe were standing outside of class. Joe said goodbye and headed north on his bicycle at the rate of 12 ft/sec. Sixty seconds later, Darlene decided to catch up with Joe. She headed north on her motor scooter at 15 ft/sec. How long will it take Darlene to catch up with Joe?

525. Darlene bought two copies of the novel *Gone With the Wind*. She suggested that each of them read it. Joe started reading his copy at the rate of 4 pages/hour. Five hours later Darlene starting reading at the rate of 14 pages/hour. How long will it take for Darlene to catch up to Joe?
(Hint: Instead of d = rt, we can use pages read = (pages/hour)(hours).)

6127. Darlene and Joe are 600 feet from each other. They run toward each other. Joe runs 80 ft/minute and Darlene runs 120 ft/minute. How long before they meet?

6405. Two cars start at the same spot. The red car heads west at 60 mph. The yellow car heads east at 50 mph. How long will it be before they are 660 miles apart?

443. Joe can make 2 pancakes/minute. After Joe had been making pancakes for 40 minutes, Darlene started making pancakes at the rate of 3 pancakes/minute. (Darlene was working on the left side of the stove and Joe on the right side.) How long would Darlene have to cook until she had made as many pancakes as Joe?

590. Joe got a sling shot for his birthday. In order to be safe, Joe would

only shoot marshmallows. Standing right next to her, he asked Darlene to throw her teddy bear up into the air, which she did at 21 ft/sec.

Two seconds later, Joe fired a marshmallow at the bear at 105 ft/sec. How long did it take the marshmallow to hit the bear?

Second part: the 𝕸ixed 𝕭ag: **a variety of problems from this chapter and previous material**

6149. What is the name of this property? $a(b + c) = ab + ac$

9230. Write $\{ x \mid x = 2n$ where n is a whole number$\}$ as a set without using set builder notation.

941. Give an example of a set that is easy to write in set builder notation, but would be very difficult to write without set builder notation.

740. Solve $9y - 36 = 6y$

957. Joe likes to play baseball with himself. Standing in the middle of a field, he threw the ball east at 16 ft/sec. After waiting 3 seconds, he started running west at 5 ft/sec. How long did he run before he and the ball were 174 feet apart?

1613. Why is it true that $5w^3 = 5w^3$?

1719. What is the smallest number in the set $\{ x \mid x = 2n + 1$ where n is a natural number$\}$?

870. $3 + 4 \cdot 6 / 12 / 3$

948. Write $\{ y \mid y$ times y equals $-36 \}$ without using set builder notation.

979. Darlene drove at 60 mph from her apartment to the Giant Bridal Mall. With her car loaded down with bridal stuff, she drove at 20 mph from the Giant Bridal Mall back to her apartment. It took 2 more hours to drive back to her apartment than it did to drive to the mall. How long did it take her to drive to the mall?

4123. What is the area of this trapezoid?

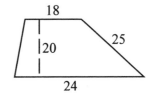

4503. In Fred's arithmetic class, he noticed that for every 8 students who used a pencil, there were 3 who used a ballpoint pen, and 1 who used a fountain pen. There were 288 students in his class. How many used ballpoint pens?

6124. Name five consecutive numbers that add to 980.

6129. Is 0.03 a rational number?

Chapter Four

First part: Problems on Each Topic

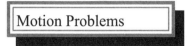

8970. Joe walked from his apartment to the ice cream store at 4 ft/sec. When he got to the store he realized that he had left his money at home and walked back to his apartment at 3 ft/sec. He walked for a total of 280 seconds to and from the store. How long did it take him to walk to the store?

9065. Darlene and Joe rented an airplane. Darlene piloted the plane at 600 mph and the rest of the time Joe flew it at 400 mph. They each flew the same distance and were in the air for a combined total of 10 hours. How long did Darlene pilot the plane?

9225. Joe had to get from his apartment to a candy factory that is 148 miles away. He went in his old car at 60 mph and then it broke down, and he walked the rest of the way to the factory at 4 mph. He walked for 5 more hours than he drove. How long did he drive?

1709. Joe got a toy parachute for his birthday. He threw it up in the air at the rate of 24 ft/sec. It floated down to his hand at the rate of 6 ft/sec. The whole round trip (up and down) took a total of 20 seconds. How many seconds was the parachute traveling upward?

Number, Rate, and Time   or   Price and Quantity

920. Joe and Darlene went into the hat decorating business. Joe decorated hats for 12 hours and Darlene decorated them for 9 hours. Darlene could decorate hats at a rate that was 10 hats/hour more than Joe's rate. They decorated the same number of hats. What was Joe's rate of decorating hats? (Hint: Let r = the number of hats/hour that Joe could decorate.)

8327. Joe and Darlene start a dog-washing business. They wash dogs in Darlene's bathtub. Joe started washing dogs at the rate of 8 dogs/hour. Then Darlene took over and started washing them at the rate of 12 dogs/hour while Joe watched television. She worked for 3 more hours than Joe had worked. Together they washed a total of 46 dogs. How long did Joe work?

1919. Inside the army transport van, Fred counted the bugs in the van at the rate of 16/minute. After a while he switched to counting pieces of gum stuck to the wall of the van at the rate of 20/minute. It was easier to count the pieces of gum since they didn't move around.

After a total of 18 minutes of counting, he had counted the same number of bugs as pieces of gum. How long had he been counting the bugs?

2272. Joe went to buy some frogs. At Diamond Frogs he paid $10/frog. At Hairy Frogs, he spent the same amount of money, but since the price was $12/frog, he bought one less frog than he did at Diamond Frogs. How many frogs did he buy at Diamond Frogs?

2900. Alexander and Betty went to a drive-in movie where they were offered Giggle Meals. Each meal consisted of one french fry (worth 5¢), one tiny drink (worth 7¢), and one ounce of french fry sauce (worth 4¢).

One Giggle Meal would hardly be enough to feed either of them. They bought a lot of those meals. The bill was $3.68. How many Giggle Meals did they buy?

Age Problems

680. Darlene is one year older than Joe. If Darlene is x years old, how old is Joe?

6122. The Song of Deborah is four times as old as the first toll road ever build in England.

Three hundred seventy-one (371) years from now the Song of Deborah will be three times as old as the road.

How old (today) is the first toll road ever built in England?

5570. The invention of the tuning fork (by trumpeter John Shore) is five times as old as Catherine Marshall's book, *A Man Called Peter*.

Thirty (30) years ago the invention of the tuning fork was nine times as old as *A Man Called Peter*.

How many years ago did Catherine Marshall write *A Man Called Peter*?

Mixture Problems

6179. Joe wants to make 30 pounds of chili seasoning that contains 30% cayenne pepper. He has one sack of mild chili seasoning that is 10% cayenne and one sack of hot chili seasoning that is 40% cayenne.

How much of each sack should he use?

6704. Darlene has some pancake mix that contains 2% sugar. She calls that her bitter mix. She has some that contains 5% sugar. She calls that her too-sweet mix.

She wants to make 60 pounds of pancake mix that has 3% sugar. How much of each mix should she use?

8975. You are a veterinarian and you need to give a marten a shot to ease its pain. You need to give it 9 cc that contains 6% morphine. You have some 4% and some 10%. How much of each should you mix together?

Side note: It is often nice in medical work to get the mathematics right. Too little pain killer and the marten remains in pain. Too much morphine and the marten will look like:

dead
marten

201. We need to ship 600 cars to Freedonia, and the order specifies that 28% of those cars should have tape players.

40% of the older cars have tape players, and 15% of the newer cars do. How many older cars should we ship?

1850. Darlene has weak dishwashing liquid that contains 17% soap. She also has strong dishwashing liquid that contains 37% soap.

Darlene just purchased a dishwashing robot. When she read the directions, she found out that the robot would only work if you gave it 444 ounces of dishwashing liquid that contained 22% soap.

How much of each dishwashing liquid should Darlene use?

(Joe never washes his dishes because he only uses paper plates.)

Second part: the 𝔐ixed 𝔅ag: a variety of problems from this chapter and previous material

2226. Joe likes his cereal with exactly 8% flour in it. (The rest is sugar and artificial flavorings.) He asked Darlene take his two boxes of cereal—Captain Mousebait (7% flour) and Sergeant Sugar (11% flour)—and mix them together to get 300 ounces.

How much of each cereal should Darlene use?

1928. Haydn wrote the "Sun" quartets five times as long ago as Robert Frost wrote "In the Clearing."

Sixteen years from now, the "Sun" quartets will be four times as old as "In the Clearing."

How old is "In the Clearing" today?

2258. Joe decided one night to read "In the Clearing." He first read the poem at the rate of 40 words/minute. Then he decided to read it backwards. Reading backwards slowed his reading rate down to 5 words/minute.

It took him a total of 27 minutes to read the poem in both directions. How long did it take Joe to read the poem in the normal direction?

2280. Joe liked to eat jelly beans while he watched television every evening. He bought red jelly beans at a cost of $5/lb. He bought green jelly beans at $6/lb. He spent a total of $488. He bought 8 more pounds of the green than of the red. How many pounds of red jelly beans did he buy?

4507. This particular cat likes some bones in his fish. (It's a good source of calcium.) This cat prefers a fish mixture with 7% bones.

How many pounds of 5% bones should he mix with 8% bones to obtain 36 pounds of fish with 7% bones?

First part: Problems on Each Topic

Solving Two Equations, Two Unknowns by Elimination

1891. Solve $\begin{cases} 7x + 3y = 43 \\ 4x - 3y = 1 \end{cases}$

2292. Solve $\begin{cases} 5x + 3y = 18 \\ -5x - 10y = 10 \end{cases}$

2904. Solve $\begin{cases} 10x + 6y = 62 \\ 8x - 2y = 2 \end{cases}$

4010. Solve $\begin{cases} 4x + 3y = 3 \\ 12x - 7y = -71 \end{cases}$

4505. Solve $\begin{cases} 6x + 6y = -18 \\ 7x + 8y = -25 \end{cases}$

4519. Solve $\begin{cases} 6x + 3y = 6 \\ 9x + 10y = 42 \end{cases}$

Union of Sets

3328. What is the union of {3, 4, 5} and {4, ♡, w}?

4280. {8} ∪ {1, 2} = ?

4500. {x | x is an integer and x > 4} ∪ {y | y is a whole number and y < 6}

600. {1, 2, 3} ∪ {3, 2, 1}

800. { } ∪ {✪}

924. For any set A, it is always true that A ∪ { } = A.

For any number x, it is always true that x times 1 equals x.

{ } is called the identity element for union.

1 is called the identity element for multiplication.

What is the identity element for addition?

1893. { y | y is an integer and y < –4} ∪ { z | z is a natural number}

Transposing

1930. Transpose the –7: $z - 7 = 44w$

2294. Transpose the 4y: $30y + 8 = 4y + 29$

2901. Transpose the variables to the left side and the numbers to the right side: $50w + 3 = 11 - w$

Graphing Points

3303. Graph (3, 7). State which quadrant that point is in.

918. Graph (–2, 10) and state which quadrant it is in.

4447. If (x, y) is in QII, what can you say about x and about y?

4520. Graph the point whose abscissa is –4 and whose ordinate is 3.

4900. If the abscissa of a point is negative, which two quadrants could that point be in?

Mean, Median, and Mode Averages

5222. What is the mean average of 6, 7, 11?

5707. What is the mode average of 3, 4, 5, 5, 5, 6, 6, 7, 7, 7 ,7, 398?

6130. What is the mean average of 0, 0, 1, 1?

6190. What is the median average of 0, 3, 4, 19, 9362?

6302. What is the mode average of 6, 9, 6, 9, 342, 6?

6417. Name three numbers whose mean average is 10.

6735. What is the median average of 7, 4, 3, 88, 555?

8340. It's easy to find the median average of an odd number of numbers. In ordinary life, if you are given a list of numbers, half of the time there will be an even number of numbers on that list. For example, 3, 8, 10, 56. Make a guess as to how to find the median average of an even number of numbers.

8900. Four people are on the bus. One of them is carrying $1000. The mean average of what those four people are carrying is $250. How much are the other three people carrying?

8977. Which of the three averages is largest for the numbers:
7, 7, 7, 7, 7, 7, 7, 7, 7, 7, 7, 7, 7, 7, 7, 7, 8?

Graphing Linear Equations

9000. What is a linear equation?

9087. Which of these equations have a graph that passes through the origin? $44x - 7y = 36$

$$200 = 30y$$

$$5x = 88y$$

208. Graph $y = 3x - 2$.

470. Graph $x = 2y + 1$.

530. Graph $2x + 3y = 6$.

999. Graph $x + y = 50$.

1633. Graph $2x + 3y = 4 + y$.

Graphing Any Equation

1721. Graph $y = x^2$.

5709. Graph $x = y^2 - 3$.

Word Problems in Two Unknowns

6207. Two rats and 5 mice cost $11.
      Four rats and 3 mice cost $15.

How much does one rat cost? How much does one mouse cost?
(Hint: Let x = cost of a rat.)

6305. Three of Dorothenia's muffins and two of her pies weigh a total of 22 pounds. Seven of her muffins and one pie weigh 33 pounds. How much does one of her muffins weigh?

8416. A bouquet of 3 daisies and 9 carnations cost $33.
A bouquet of 4 daisies and 7 carnations cost $29.
How much does each flower cost?

Chapter Five

Second part: the 𝔐ixed 𝔅ag: a variety of problems from this chapter and previous material

950. $\{\ \} \cup \{x \mid x \text{ is an antelope}\}$

6414. Solve $\begin{cases} 2x + 5y = 35 \\ 5x + 9y = 77 \end{cases}$

1832. Graph $y = x^3$.

6150. Graph $x = y^2 + y$.

2935. Solve $\begin{cases} 5x + 2y = -6 \\ 6x + 5y = 11 \end{cases}$

4522. Find the mean average of $-8, -3, 0, 31$.

6210. What is the union of the whole numbers and the natural numbers?

6308. For every 3 pizzas I eat, I gain 2 pounds. What is the ratio of pizzas to pounds?

6418. Name a value for x that will make $5 < x < 6$ true. (Hint: x will not be a natural number.)

6738. The equality of two ratios is called a _____ ?
fill in one word

7023. What is the coefficient of x^{20}?

7800. Graph $y = 0.5x^2$.

8004. Stanthony's medium pizza is 21" in diameter. What is its circumference? (In this problem, use 22/7 for π.)

8207. In 58 minutes, Joe can wash 3 cars and 4 dogs. In 99 minutes, he can wash 5 cars and 7 dogs. How long does it take him to wash a car, and how long does it take him to wash a dog?

1222. What is the mode average of 33, 34, 34, 35, 77, 77, 77, 298?

8915. The point (c, d) is directly above (6, 7). What can you say about the values of c and d?

9011. Graph $y = -4$.

4282. What is the median average of 10, 11, 11.3, 11.7, 11.8?

2939. You multiply together nine numbers. No two of them are equal. The answer is equal to zero. Three of the numbers are positive. How many are negative?

1933. If a rectangle has an area of 56 square inches, and its length is 8 inches, what is the length of the perimeter?

Chapter Six

First part: Problems on Each Topic

Solving Two Equations, Two Unknowns by Graphing

2300. Solve by graphing $\begin{cases} -2x + y = 1 \\ y = -3x + 16 \end{cases}$

2909. Solve by graphing $\begin{cases} y = 3x + 5 \\ 4x + y = -15 \end{cases}$

2941. One pull up and three pushups takes 25 Calories.

Three pull ups and two pushups takes 33 Calories. Solving by graphing, determine how many Calories a pull up and a pushup each take.

Exponents

51. $x^{20}x^3$

5712. $\dfrac{y^6}{y^2}$

6277. $(z^4)^8$

6311. $(10w^8)^6$

6420. 5^{-2}

9306. $\dfrac{x^7y^3}{x^2y}$

9012. $\dfrac{a^{55}b^{20}c}{a^{33}b^{30}c}$

8418. $(6x^2y^{-3})^5$

7030. $(532a^{32987}b^{-3}cd^{3.53}e^{-1})^0$

7788. $z^2z^4z^3$

7306. $(xyz^6)^4$

6742. $\dfrac{x^{-5}y^3}{x^2y^{-9}}$

6800. Which is larger: 0^1 or 1^0?

Solving Two Equations, Two Unknowns by Substitution

6902. Solve by substitution $\begin{cases} y = 5x + 2 \\ 6x + 2y = 52 \end{cases}$

6315. Solve by substitution $\begin{cases} 3x + 2y = 19 \\ x = -5y - 11 \end{cases}$

5588. Solve by substitution $\begin{cases} 2x + 6y = -4 \\ 7x + 16y = 1 \end{cases}$

5792. Ten apples and three bananas cost 155¢. It is an even trade if you exchange one apple for two bananas and 4¢.

x¢   y¢

Using two equations and two unknowns and solving by substitution determine how much one apple costs.

Inconsistent and Dependent Equations

5225. You were trying to solve a pair of linear equations by graphing, and the graph looked like this.

What can you say about those equations?

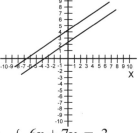

1894. Solve by elimination $\begin{cases} 6x + 7y = 3 \\ -6x - 7y = 1 \end{cases}$

1935. Solve by graphing $\begin{cases} 3x - 3 = 9y \\ x - 3y = 1 \end{cases}$

2100. Solve by elimination $\begin{cases} 8x + 12y = 20 \\ 2x + 3y = 5 \end{cases}$

2305. Inconsistent equations can make you rich. Let s = price of a silver coin, and let g = the price of a gold coin. Suppose one silver coin and two gold coins can be bought or sold for $1700 in New York, and can be bought or sold for $2000 in London. Show that $s + 2g = 1700$ and $s + 2g = 2000$ are inconsistent, and I will show you how to get rich.

Commutative Laws

22. Give three examples of the commutative law of multiplication.

243. Why is this not an example of the commutative law of multiplication: $55 + 23 = 23 + 55$?

402. Show that there is no such thing as the commutative law of subtraction.

501. Is there such a thing as the commutative law of division?

541. Are the acts of baking a pizza and eating it commutative?

Factorials and Ordering

805. Evaluate 6!

871. How much bigger is 34! than 33! ?

1316. Evaluate 1!!!!!

1375. Scientific calculators are the calculators that have "sin" and "log" and "!" on them. Many of them can do up to 69! before they quit. If you have such a calculator, evaluate 4!!. You do that by entering 4 and then hitting the ! twice. (If you don't own one of those calculators, be on the lookout for sales. As of this writing, I've seen them as cheap as $15. You will need one for Advanced Algebra and Trig.)

1602. How many times bigger is 8!! than the total number of possible chess games? Namely, how many times bigger is $10^{168,186}$ than 10^{120}?

1667. You need to pick out one of four hats for the party you are going to and then put on one of three watches that you have. How many different ways can you do those two things?

1725. Sergeant Snow had six different favorite pancakes: maple, blueberry, chocolate, oatmeal, strawberry, and cinnamon. He liked to have the cook put one of each kind into a single stack. How many different ways could the cook stack those six pancakes?

Negative and Zero Exponents

1834. Express without a negative exponent: x^{-5}.

1936. Evaluate 3962^1.

2308. Evaluate 3962^0.

2400. Express as a decimal: 10^{-3}.

2500. Simplify as much as possible: $(\frac{1}{3})^{-3}$

2603. Simplify as much as possible: $(\frac{5}{6})^{-2}$

Volumes

2717. What is the volume of a cube that is 3 feet on each edge?

2788. What is the volume of a sphere (a ball) that has a radius of 5 inches? (Use 3 for π in this problem.)

2943. What is the exact volume of a sphere that has a diameter of 8 miles?

3366. What is the volume of a pot that has a radius of 6 inches and a height of 10 inches? (Use 3 for π in this problem.)

4450. If you took a party hat and turned it upside down and filled it with root beer, how many cubic inches would it hold? (Use 3 for π in this problem.)

This hat is 7 inches tall and has a radius of 4 inches.

Chapter Six

Second part: the 𝔐ixed 𝔅ag: a variety of problems from this chapter and previous material

2777. Does the graph of $y = 3x^5 - 0.07x + 1$ pass through the origin?

7116. Which is larger: 2^6 or 6^2?

4530. $(10x^4z^5)^6$

4700. Solve by elimination
$$\begin{cases} 3x + 4y = 4 \\ 4x + 5y = 6 \end{cases}$$

4818. Solve the equations in the previous problem by graphing.

4909. Solve by substitution
$$\begin{cases} 2x + 3y = 1 \\ y = 3x + 26 \end{cases}$$

5231. If n is odd, what is the next consecutive odd number after n?

5590. Write $\{\, y \mid y = 2n \text{ where n is a whole number} \,\}$ without using set builder notation.

5600. Twenty-five years ago, Pat was twice as old as Chris. Today, Pat is five years older than Chris. What is Pat's present age?

5300. Joe went out for a walk in the woods. When he was in the woods, he could spot bunnies on a pogo sticks at the rate of 4 per minute.

When Joe got to the street, he saw bunnies painting lines on the street. He spent 30 fewer minutes on the street than in the woods. Bunnies painting lines were easier to spot. He saw them at the rate of 6 per minute.

He spotted the same number of each kind of bunny. How long was he in the woods spotting hopping bunnies?

3005. $\{6, 7, 123\} \cup \{6, A\}$

3370. $(\sin 76^\circ + \log 3.998 + \sqrt{888}\,)^0$

4284. Solve by elimination:
$$\begin{cases} 5x - 6y = 32 \\ -10x + 12y = -64 \end{cases}$$

4468. $\dfrac{100!}{99!}$

4531. Evaluate $2!!!$

4711. Are opening your mouth and brushing your teeth commutative?

4820. Joe bought a giant can of beans. Its diameter was 12 inches and its height was 10 inches. First, find the volume of that can (using 3 for π in this problem), and then convert that to quarts. (There are roughly 58 cubic inches in a quart.) Round your answer to the nearest quart.

37

5000. Is it correct to write {3} + {22}? If so, give the answer. If not, explain why it is not correct.

5598. Using braces, list the set of integers.

5606. 64 − (−8)

5795. Express 44 ÷ 13 as a ratio.

6215. Is it true that −14 < −100?

6288. If you multiply six negative numbers together, what will be the sign of the answer?

6320. Draw a picture of a circle and then draw a radius.

6421. What is the coefficient of πx^4? (Hint: The answer is not 1.)

6500. −56/−8

6748. Name three consecutive odd numbers that add to 1881.

6811. Is every natural number a rational number?

3037. Is zero a rational number?

7120. Darlene is hard on shoes. She wears them out very quickly. She wears out her dress shoes at the rate of 5/month. She wears out her sneakers at the rate of 3/month.

When she turned 16, she started wearing dress shoes. After several months, she switched over and started just wearing sneakers.

When she had worn sneakers for six more months than she wore dress shoes, she had worn out the same number of each. How long did she wear dress shoes?

7309. Express without negative exponents $\dfrac{x^{-5}y}{x^6 y^{-4}}$

7790. Joe bought this giant golf ball at a garage sale. It has a diameter of 8 inches. What is its volume? (Use 3 for π in this problem.)

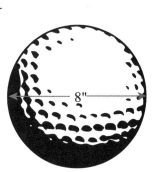

(It should be quite difficult to play golf with this ball. It won't fit in the hole.)

Chapter Seven

First part: Problems on Each Topic

Multiplying Binomials and Trinomials

7403. $(5x + 3)(4x + 7)$
300. $(2x - 6)(x - 8)$
7606. $(8y + 2)(3y - 9)$
2504. $(w^4 + 5)(w^3 - 7)$
2606. $(3x + 4y)(5x + 8y)$
2790. $(2x + 5y)(3x + 4y + 10z)$
2946. $(x + y)(x + 2y)$
3211. $(a + b + c + d)(a + b + c + d)$
3404. $(x + y)^2$
3502. $(a + b + c)^2$
3601. $(7x + 3y)(7x - 3y)$
4017. $(7x + 3y)(7x + 3y)$

Polynomials

4275. Fill in the blanks: A **polynomial** is an expression formed by _____, _____, or _____ numbers and letters.

4470. Which of these are polynomials? x, 0, $\dfrac{w + y + 2}{17}$, $\dfrac{v}{\pi}$, $\dfrac{\pi}{v}$

4600. $7 + 5$ is a polynomial with two terms.

   12 is a polynomial with one term.

A binomial is a polynomial with two terms.

A monomial is a polynomial with one term.

Easy question: Can a binomial equal a monomial?

4712. A trinomial is a polynomial with three terms. Give an example of a trinomial that is equal to a monomial.

4822. To count the number of terms in a polynomial, draw big vertical lines at + or – signs where the pieces that result make sense.

For example: 3 + 4xy – 55xyz can be broken into three terms:

3 ▌4xy ▌55xyz is broken into 3, 4xy, and 55xyz

—all of which make sense. It is a trinomial.

In contrast, $\frac{x\ +\ y}{6}$ can't be divided by a big vertical line where the pieces would make sense.

If I try, $\frac{x\ ▐\ y}{6}$ would give $\frac{x}{}$ which doesn't make sense.

Another way to define what a *term* is, would be to say that it is an expression that is formed by combining numbers and/or letters using only multiplication.

This all gets tooooo complicated.

These are monomials: 38, xy, $9236492983.3z^{9792392}$

These are binomials: $4 + x$, $w^8 – 5$, $a + b$

These are trinomials: $a + 3xy + c$, $\pi – 27x – 40$, $55 + 235x + \frac{w}{6}$

Your question: Did I define what a **term** is in the *Life of Fred: Beginning Algebra Expanded Edition* book when I defined monomials, binomials, and trinomials?

First Kind of Factoring: Common Factors

4911. Factor $6x + 8y$

5100. Factor $10x^2 + 15xy^4$

5201. Factor $12wx^3 – 16w^2x^5$

5302. Factor $6x^4y^4z^4 + 9xy^7z^3$

5450. Factor $24xy^2z^3 + 36xy^4z^2 + 48x^5y^2z^2$

5592. Factor $18aby – 25bxy$

358. There are five kinds of factoring covered in this Chapter 7: Common factors; Easy Trinomials (of the form $x^2 + bx + c$); Difference of Squares; Grouping; and Harder Trinomials (of the form $ax^2 + bx + c$ where $a \neq 1$). Which of these five should you always look for first?

Chapter Seven

Factoring Easy Trinomials (of the form $x^2 + bx + c$)

407. Factor $x^2 + 44x + 66x^5$
522. Factor $x^2 + 13x + 22$
544. Factor $y^2 + 10y + 25$
807. Factor $w^2 + 15w + 56$
873. Factor $x^2 + 3x - 54$
951. Factor $24x^2 + 24x + 48$
1003. Factor $z^2 + 15z + 50$
1099. Factor $x^2 - 2x - 15$
1200. Factor $y^2 - 6y - 16$
1280. Factor $x^2 + 20x + 36$
1387. Factor $w^2 + 6w - 40$
1520. Factor $x^2 - 15x - 100$

Difference of Squares Factoring

1635. Factor $16x^2 - 32$
1680. Factor $x^2 - 25$
1726. Factor $100x^2 - 49$
1898. Factor $4x^2 + 25$
1939. Factor $36y^2 - z^2$
2000. Factor $x^6 - 100$
1750. Factor $7w^2 - 49$
2050. Factor $9x^{40} - y^8z^8$
2310. Factor completely $x^4 - 16$.
2506. Factor $z^4 + 16$
2390. Factor $w^4 - 81$

Factoring by Grouping

2608. Factor $6x^2 + 3xw + 8x + 4w$
2800. Factor $x^3 - 5x^2 + 4x - 20$
2949. Factor $2x^2y - 10x^2w - 7y + 35w$

3162. Factor $x^2y - 2x^2 + 8xy - 16x + 15y - 30$

(Hint: In this case, try grouping the first two, the second two, and the last two.)

3009. Factor $x^5y^2 - 9x^5 + 3y^2 - 27$

3215. Factor $2wy^2 + 2wy - 60w - 3y^2 - 3y + 90$

(Hint: In this case, try grouping the first three terms and the last three terms.) **I, your reader, have a question. How am I suppose to know whether to group six terms into 2 terms + 2 terms + 2 terms or into 3 terms + 3 terms? What's the rule?**

I, your author, would also like to know the rule. I try one way, and if it doesn't work, I try the other way. Sometimes, I even rearrange the terms and see if that works. I know the two rules of life, but I don't know the rule for grouping polynomials with six terms.

3260. Factor $9x^4 + 54x^2 - x^2y^2 - 6y^2$

3380. Factor $x^2y^2 - 2x^2y - 15x^2 + 8xy^2 - 16xy - 120x + 7y^2 - 14y - 105$

Factoring Harder Trinomials (of the form $ax^2 + bx + c$ where a ≠ 1)

3606. Factor $5w^2 + 13w + 6$

4000. Factor $8x^2 - 13x - 6$

3407. Factor $3x^2 + 13x + 4$

3505. Factor $12y^2 + 51y + 45$

4260. Factor $4x^2 - 4x - 15$

4350. Factor $6y^4 + 19y^2 + 10$

4477. Factor $2x^2 + 63x + 5$

4290. Factor $20z^2 + 11z - 9$

4533. Factor $35x^2 + 13x - 4$

Solving Quadratic Equations by Factoring

4603. What's a quadratic equation?

4699. Solve $x^2 - 2x = 35$

4829. Solve $x^2 - 56 = -x$

4913. Solve $6x^2 - x = 15$

5001. Solve $x^2 - 36 = 0$

Chapter Seven

5597. Solve $10xw - 45x + 12w = 54$

5609. We started with a square where each side was s centimeters long.

We increased one side by 3 centimeters and decreased the other side by 4 centimeters. The resulting rectangle had an area of 60 square centimeters. What is the length of a side of the original square?

5790. Solve $30x^3 + 5x = -31x^2$

4020. Solve $2x^2 + 7 - 5x = 7$

5800. Solve $x^3 - 4x^2 + 3x = 12$

6019. In a right triangle the shortest leg is 10 meters shorter than the other leg. The hypotenuse is 50 meters long. How long is the shorter leg?

Second part: the 𝕸ixed 𝕭ag: a variety of problems from this chapter and previous material

4125. Factor $81x^4 - 1$

4824. Factor $20ac + 8ad + 15bc + 6bd$

6111. Stanthony's personal-sized pizza has a diameter that is 8 inches less than the Stanthony's pizza-for-two. The pizza-for-two is 80π square inches larger than the personal-sized pizza. What is the diameter of the personal-sized pizza?

4030. Factor $x^2y^6 - 49$

3700. List a set that has a cardinality of 7.

3855. Fill in the blank: $-54 + \underline{\quad} = 4$

3927. Why is it true that $888 + \log 7 = 888 + \log 7$?

4127. Solve $12z^2 + 5z = 2$

4295. Solve $\begin{cases} 5x - 2y = -3 \\ 7x + 5y = -51 \end{cases}$

4354. $(3x + 5w)^2 = ?$

4399. Darlene can grow 50 carrots in each square meter of her garden. Joe doesn't water his garden as often as Darlene. He can grow only 40 carrots per square meter. His garden is 2 square meters larger than hers. They grow the same number of carrots. How large is her garden?

4535. Is 4xy a monomial, binomial, or a trinomial?

4607. Factor $w^2 - 3w - 18$

4716. Jackie is four times as old as Dale.
In $2\frac{1}{8}$ years, Jackie will be three times as old as Dale.
How old is Dale today?

4831. Factor $14x^2 + 27x - 20$

5004. Darlene liked to draw faces, but
she was slow. Joe worked at a rate of
6 faces per minutes more than Darlene.
In 4 minutes he drew as many faces as
Darlene did in 12 minutes.
How fast could Darlene draw faces?

5107. Joe likes jelly beans where 9% of them are green. That makes him
happiest. He has one jar that has 4% green jelly beans and another jar that
has 16%. How much of each jar should he combine to make 24 kilograms
where 9% of them are green? (Since a kilogram is a little over two
pounds, that may seem like a lot of jelly beans, but Joe consumes an
inordinate amount of jelly beans.)

5203. Find the mean, median, and mode averages for 4, 5, 6, 8, 8.

5111. $\{\heartsuit, \diamondsuit, \clubsuit\} \cup \{\heartsuit, \diamondsuit, \spadesuit\}$

5234. Graph $y = 4x - 2$

5215. $8 + 4/2$

5304. Darlene's uncle had a square piece of land in Oklahoma. He
bought more acreage that enlarged his original square into a rectangle.
One side was now 1 mile larger than the original square. The other side
was 3 miles larger than the original square. He now had 120 square miles
of land. What were the dimensions of the original square?

5236. Is $6x + 395x^2 - 17$ a quadratic equation?

5101. Solve $10x^2 + 29x = -10$

5009. Factor $2x^2 - 112 - 2x$

4835. If you are trying to factor a binomial, what kind of factoring should
you look for first?

4610. Darlene's aunt is three times as old as Darlene. Twenty-one years
from now, Darlene's aunt will be twice as old as Darlene will be. How old
is Darlene today?

Chapter Eight

First part: Problems on Each Topic

Equations Containing Fractions

4580. Solve $\dfrac{1}{5x} + \dfrac{1}{2x} = \dfrac{7}{30}$

4360. Solve $\dfrac{x-1}{3} - \dfrac{1}{6} = \dfrac{x-3}{2}$

8008. Solve $\dfrac{y}{y+1} - \dfrac{3}{y+1} = \dfrac{4}{y^2+y}$

7803. Solve $6x = \dfrac{10}{x} + 7$

2566. Solve $\dfrac{x+13}{x^2-29} = 1$

Simplifying Fractions

2950. Simplify $\dfrac{x^2-81}{x+9}$

3114. Simplify $\dfrac{y^2-y-12}{y^2-16}$

3262. Simplify $\dfrac{14x^2+23x+3}{10xw+2x+15w+3}$

3508. Simplify $\dfrac{9x^4-y^8}{3x+y^2}$

3705. Simplify $\dfrac{8x^2+2x-15}{14x^2+21x}$

953. Simplify $\dfrac{x(x+3)-5(x+3)}{4x^2-13x-35}$

Adding and Subtracting Fractions

3900. $\dfrac{4}{3x^2y^3} + \dfrac{5}{7xy^6}$

1060. $\dfrac{4}{x-9} + \dfrac{2}{x-3}$

6021. $\dfrac{5}{y-12} + \dfrac{17-y}{12-y}$

3610. $\dfrac{x}{x+2} + \dfrac{-12}{x^2-2x-8}$

3870. $\dfrac{5}{x-7} - \dfrac{70}{x^2-49}$

3424. $\dfrac{6}{5x} + 7$

2954. $\dfrac{2}{x^2-2x-15} + \dfrac{7}{x^2-13x+40}$

3222. $\dfrac{6}{x^2+3x} + \dfrac{5x}{x^2-2x-15}$

3393. $\dfrac{2x^2+19x+48}{(x-4)(x+3)(x+2)} + \dfrac{9}{x^2-x-12} + \dfrac{3}{x+2}$

Multiplying and Dividing Fractions

3965. $\dfrac{x+3}{x+2} \times \dfrac{x^2-4}{x^2+5x+6}$

4401. $\dfrac{y^2-1}{8} \times \dfrac{6}{(y+1)^2} \times \dfrac{y^2+4y+3}{(y-1)^2}$

5117. $\dfrac{4x^2-1}{3x+4} \div \dfrac{2x^2+9x-5}{3x^2+19x+20}$

5240. $\dfrac{(w+40)^8}{(w-40)^2} \div \dfrac{(w+40)^2}{w-40}$

Complex Fractions (Fractions within Fractions)

1753. $$\dfrac{\dfrac{2x^2 - 7x - 30}{30x^2 - 30x - 600}}{\dfrac{x^2 - 36}{5x + 20}}$$

1835. $$\dfrac{\dfrac{y^2 + 13y + 40}{y^2 - 7y - 44}}{\dfrac{2y^2 + 13y - 24}{2y^2 - 25y + 33}}$$

2056. $$\dfrac{\dfrac{3}{x + 2} - \dfrac{3x + 1}{x^2 + 5x + 6}}{\dfrac{7}{x + 5} - \dfrac{7x + 4}{x^2 + 7x + 10}}$$

Job Problems

2403. Joe can paint a room in 5 hours. Darlene could paint the same room in 3 hours.
How long would it take to paint the room if they worked together?

2960. Alexander can unload a boxcar full of books in 2 days. Betty can unload it in 3 days. It takes Joe 20 days to unload the boxcar. If all three work together, how long would it take them to unload a boxcar full of books?

3430. Darlene decided to build a rowboat for Joe for his birthday. She and Betty could build it together in 3 months. Betty working alone could build it in 4 months. How long would it take Darlene to build it alone?

Second part: the 𝕸ixed 𝕭ag: a variety of problems from this chapter and previous material

4537. Solve $\dfrac{2}{3} + \dfrac{1}{x+7} = \dfrac{x+15}{15}$

3858. Simplify $\dfrac{w^8 - 16}{w^3 - 2w^2 + 4w - 8}$

3960. $\dfrac{7}{4x^{10}y^2} + \dfrac{12}{6xy^9}$

1100. Joe and Darlene had a running contest. They each ran for 20 seconds. Darlene can run 3 ft/sec faster than Joe. Together they ran a total of 260 feet. How fast did Joe run? (No credit will be given unless you begin with Let r = . . . or use Six Pretty boxes.)

4363. $\dfrac{\dfrac{12-y}{y^2 - 9y + 20} + \dfrac{1}{y-4}}{\dfrac{2}{y+6} + \dfrac{31 - 2y}{y^2 + y - 30}}$

3411. $\dfrac{7y^2 + 47y + 18}{(y+2)(y+5)(y-1)} - \dfrac{7}{(y+2)(y+5)} - \dfrac{4}{y-1}$

2727. Solve $\dfrac{2}{y+2} + \dfrac{1}{y+5} = \dfrac{21}{y^2 + 7y + 10}$

3850. Evaluate 3!!

3955. $80 + \dfrac{2}{w}$

6323. A hiker went to collect 1000 wild flowers for his girl friend. She wanted 20% of them to be red. The lower trail had 15% red flowers and the upper trail had 35% red flowers. (He was color blind.) How many flowers should he pick from the lower trail?

53. Are two sets equal if they have the same number of elements?

2051. $\dfrac{\dfrac{x^2 + 9x + 18}{2x^2 + 13x + 20}}{\dfrac{x^2 + 2x - 24}{x^2 - 16}}$

58. $-25 + (-77) + 30$

205. Express $44 \div 7$ as a ratio.

245. What is the cardinality of $\{8.29872\}$?

360. Is it possible to find a positive number w such that $w^2 < w$?

370. If a circle has a radius of 8 meters, what is its exact circumference?

436. If some number times -83 is equal to a positive answer, what can you say about that number?

547. Factor $20y^2 - 39y + 18$

875. Joe likes to draw with crayons. He can use up a whole box of  crayons in 6 hours. Darlene likes to use crayons to fill out coupons in her bridal magazines. She can use up a whole box in 3 hours.

   Working together, how long would it take them to use up a whole box of crayons?

810. A pizza has a circumference of 44". What is its diameter? Use $\dfrac{22}{7}$ for π.

2001. Joe likes to watch the circus on television. His three favorite acts are the goat, the dog and the elephant. For every 5 hours of watching goat acts, he watched 7 hours of dog acts and 8 hours of elephant acts.

   All together, he watched 4,000 hours of these three types of acts. How many hours did he watch each of them?

Chapter Nine

First part: Problems on Each Topic

Simplifying Square Roots

523. Simplify $\sqrt{12}$

3012. Simplify $\sqrt{27}$

3121. Simplify $\sqrt{300}$

3716. Simplify $5\sqrt{7} + 26\sqrt{7}$

4150. Simplify $\sqrt{20} + \sqrt{45}$

4321. Simplify $\sqrt{63} + \sqrt{81} + \sqrt{28}$

Solving Pure Quadratic Equations

1900. What's a pure quadratic equation?

2060. Solve $x^2 = 64$

2323. Solve $z^2 = 1$

2407. Write a pure quadratic equation that had exactly one solution.

2570. Solve $5x^2 = 500$

3620. If we have a right triangle in which the legs are 5 feet and 12 feet, how long is the hypotenuse?

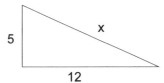

4141. Solve $7x^2 - 400 = 3x^2$

2611. In a right triangle, the hypotenuse is equal to 9, and one leg is equal to 4. What is the length of the other leg?

Principal Square Roots

4538. Name the square roots of 64.

4611. Name the principal square root of 9.

4718. Is there any situation in which a number can have more than one principal square root?

4848. Could $\sqrt{144}$ equal -12?

5252. If $x^2 = 36$, then would it be correct to write $x = \sqrt{36}$?

5311. Suppose you are told that $\sqrt{x} = y$ (where x and y are real numbers). Real numbers are numbers on the number line:

The Real Numbers

What can you say about x? What can you say about y?

The Real Numbers and the Irrational Numbers

5799. Is it true that the square of every real number is positive?

6025. What is the name of this set? $\{x \mid x = a/b$ where a and b are integers and $b \neq 0\}$

6234. It is true that every real number is either rational or irrational. Is it true that every real number is either positive or negative?

6290. This is a hard problem. We know that π is irrational. That means that it cannot be expressed as a/b where a and b are integers and $b \neq 0$. Make an argument to show that 7π must be irrational.

Cube Roots and Indexes

6505. What is the radicand of $\sqrt{5432xyz}$?

6344. What is the index of $\sqrt[3]{8xy}$?

7225. Simplify $\sqrt[3]{64}$

303. Simplify $\sqrt[3]{-125}$

Fractional and Negative Exponents

9275. Express without negative exponents: x^{-5}

9073. Simplify $100^{1/2}$

8919. Simplify 100^{-2}

8700. Simplify $100^{-1/2}$

1225. Simplify $\dfrac{x^7 + x^{-2}}{x^{-3}}$

8210. Simplify $\dfrac{x^{-2} + y^{-3}}{z^6}$ (This can be turned into a complex fraction.)

Solving Radical Equations

7425. Solve $3 = \sqrt{x - 7}$

5010. Solve $\sqrt{41 - x} = 6$

4747. Solve $\sqrt{x + 72} - 4 = 5$

3979. Solve $\sqrt{13 - x} - x = 7$

3720. Solve $\sqrt{64 + y} - 28 = y - 20$

4940. Solve $\sqrt{x + 12} = -4$

Rationalizing the Denominator

For each of the following, simplify by rationalizing the denominator.

4545. $\dfrac{7}{\sqrt{n}}$

248. $\dfrac{4x}{\sqrt{5x}}$

1007. $\dfrac{31y}{\sqrt{x + 3y}}$

1069. $\dfrac{2}{\sqrt{w} + 5}$

6509. $\dfrac{y + \sqrt{z}}{\sqrt{z}}$

6825. $\dfrac{\sqrt{x} + \sqrt{y}}{\sqrt{x} - \sqrt{y}}$

Chapter Nine

Second part: the 𝔐ixed 𝔅ag: a variety of problems from this chapter and previous material

3512. In a right triangle, the hypotenuse is equal to 9, and one leg is equal to 6. What is the length of the other leg? Simplify your answer (but do not approximate it).

4300. Solve $6y^2 + 600 = 11y^2 - 400$

4838. Simplify $\sqrt{44} + \sqrt{99} + \sqrt{11}$

5595. What values of x make this true: $\sqrt{x} = x$.

868. $$\dfrac{\dfrac{2}{x^2 - x - 6} - \dfrac{5}{x^2 - 7x + 12} + \dfrac{6x^2 - 39x + 90}{(x + 2)(x - 3)(x - 4)}}{\dfrac{5}{x^2 - x - 6} + \dfrac{2x - 1}{(x^2 - 2x - 8)(x - 3)}}$$

5692. What values of x make $\sqrt{-x} = 5$ true?

6424. What is the name of this set? $\{\, x \mid x$ is a real number that cannot be written as a/b where a and b are integers and $b \neq 0\}$

6303. Joe and Darlene decided to drive a tractor. Joe could drive it at 4 mph. Darlene at 6 mph. Joe drove it first and then let Darlene drive it. Together, they drove the tractor 12 hours and covered 67 miles. How long did Joe drive it?

7412. If the index of a radical is 4, can the radicand be negative?

867. Simplify $\sqrt[3]{1000}$

7814. Simplify $\dfrac{w^7}{x^{-3} - z^4}$

6304. In a right triangle, the hypotenuse is equal to 15, and one leg is equal to 10. What is the length of the other leg? Simplify your answer (but do not approximate it).

4912. Solve $\sqrt{x + 14} = 4$

4860. Simplify by rationalizing the denominator $\dfrac{x + y}{\sqrt{6xy}}$

4650. Factor $8x^2 + 16x + 32$

7700. A red mouse can eat all the turnovers in my pantry in 6 hours. A blue mouse can eat them all in 6 hours. A green mouse can eat them all in 3 hours. If all three work on my turnovers, how soon would they all be gone?

4326. If the diameter of a circle is 18 inches. What is its exact circumference?

4965. Your net worth was –$300 in January and after your paycheck it became $700. How much was your paycheck?

5017. Express 6/11 as a ratio.

5266. By the symmetric law of equality, what would $4x^3 = 55$ become?

5607. Solve $3x - 5 = 7x - 11$

3550. Roger took his son Eddie out to practice shooting arrows. He set up a paper target to make things "realistic." Together they shot 600 arrows and 180 of them hit the target.

Six percent of Eddie's shots hit the target and 56% of Roger's hit the target.

How many arrows did Eddie shoot?

2888. We know that every fraction can be expressed as a repeating decimal. For example, $\frac{3}{4} = 0.7500000000000$ and $\frac{2}{3} = 0.666666....$

How would you go about converting $\frac{37}{123}$ into a repeating decimal?

(You don't have to actually do it. Just explain how you would do it.)

4330. Let's do something new. You know how to change a fraction into a repeating decimal. (You just did it in the previous problem.)

Here's how to go the other direction and change a repeating decimal into a fraction.

Suppose you are given: 0.147147147147....

Let x = 0.147147147147...   (line 1)

Then 1000x = 147.147147147147....   (line 2)

(We chose 1000 to make line 1 and line 2 match up.)

Subtract line 1 from line 2: 999x = 147.0000000

Divide by 999:   x = 147/999

Now you do it: Change 0.338838338338 . . . into a fraction.

$$Chapter\ Ten$$

First part: Problems on Each Topic

Solving Quadratic Equations by Completing the Square

4977. What number do you add to $x^2 + 12x$ to make it into a perfect square?

5020. What number do you add to $x^2 + 20x$ to make it into a perfect square? After you have added that number, factor the resulting trinomial.

1683. What number do you add to $x^2 - 18x$ to make it into a perfect square? After you have added that number, factor the resulting trinomial.

1942. Solve $x^2 + 5x - 36 = 0$ by factoring and then solve it by completing the square.

2340. When you did the previous problem, it took about three times as long to solve $x^2 + 5x - 36 = 0$ by completing the square as it did by factoring. We learned how to solve quadratic equations by factoring in Chapter 8. Why did we introduce solving quadratic equations by completing the square in this Chapter 10?

2410. Solve $x^2 + 4x - 7 = 0$ by completing the square.

2575. Solve $3x^2 + 6x - 23 = 0$ by completing the square.

2615. Simplify and combine $-1 \pm \sqrt{\dfrac{26}{3}}$

1903. Solve $12x + 7 = 6x^2$ by completing the square.

Quadratic Formula

594. Solve $2x^2 + 5x + 1 = 0$

1009. Solve $5x^2 + 9x = -3$

495. Solve $6x^2 - 7x - 5 = 0$

1044. Solve $3x^2 + 4x + 5 = 0$

1010. Solve $10x^2 + 10x - 30 = 0$

1252. Solve $x^2 + 3x - 6 = 5x$

1945. Multiple choice: We used completing the square to go from the standard equation $ax^2 + bx + c = 0$ to $x = \dfrac{-b \pm \sqrt{b^2 - 4ac}}{2a}$

in the *Life of Fred: Beginning Algebra Expanded Edition* book. (Do you remember those "pain circles" that surrounded the derivation?)

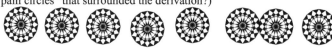

That seems like a lot of work just to get the formula. (It was.)

Now your question: Why did we teach completing the square?

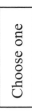

A) *We did it just to get the quadratic formula. It was just done to inflict pain on the reader.*

B) *There was a second reason mentioned in the textbook why we learned completion of the square.*

C) *There has gotta be another use for completing the square, but it wasn't mentioned in the text.*

1378. Solve $x^2 + 4x - 2 = 0$ Simplify your answer.

5611. Solve $3x + 4x^2 = -1$

5050. Look at the quadratic formula for a second. $x = \dfrac{-b \pm \sqrt{b^2 - 4ac}}{2a}$

We will have no solution when $b^2 - 4ac$ is negative.

Which of these quadratic equations have no solution?

A) $6x^2 - 4x + 1 = 0$

B) $2x^2 + 5x + 5 = 0$

C) $4x^2 + 10x + 31 = 0$

D) $5x^2 - 7x - 3 = 0$

6115. Will this quadratic equation have a solution?

$9926492390262x^2 - 343590003027x - 98929939946369282862 = 0$

Please! Don't do the arithmetic. Just looking at $b^2 - 4ac$ you can tell whether it's going to be positive or negative.

6325. Look at the quadratic formula for a second. $x = \dfrac{-b \pm \sqrt{b^2 - 4ac}}{2a}$

Usually, there will be two different values of x that will make the equation true. Viz.,* $x = (-b + \sqrt{b^2 - 4ac})/2a$ and $x = (-b - \sqrt{b^2 - 4ac})/2a$. When will there be exactly one value of x that makes $ax^2 + bx + c = 0$ true?

---

* Viz. is the standard abbreviation for *videlicet* (we-DAY-le-kit) just as etc. is the standard abbreviation for et cetera. In case you're wondering, *videlicet* is Latin for *namely.*

Long Division of Polynomials

6498. $4x + 6\overline{)8x^3 + 12x + 77}$

6831. $3x + 2\overline{)6x^3 - 5x^2}$

3015. $5x - 4\overline{)25x^3 + 5x^2 - 5x}$

251. $x - 1\overline{)x^4 - 1}$

642. $x^2 - 4\overline{)x^4 - 16}$

992. $6x - 5\overline{)12x^3 + 8x^2 + 21x - 28}$

Second part: the 𝔐ixed 𝔅ag: a variety of problems from this chapter and previous material

1904. Change 0.77327732773277327732 . . . into a fraction.

Hint: Use 10000x instead of 1000x in order to move the decimal over four places.

650. Does $\frac{22}{7}$ equal π?

2066. Simplify by rationalizing the denominator. $\dfrac{6}{3 - \sqrt{z}}$

2301. Solve $\sqrt{5x + 4} + 2 = x$

2507. If the circumference of a circle is equal to 4 feet, what is its exact diameter?

2745. Simplify $\dfrac{w^{-5} + w^7 x^{-2}}{w^{30} x^{40}}$

3020. Solve $2x^2 + 75 = 5x^2$

2890. Simplify $\sqrt[3]{1000}$

2508. $\dfrac{\dfrac{3x^2 + 22x - 16}{x + 7}}{\dfrac{x^2 - 49}{x^2 + 11x + 24}}$

1040. Simplify $\sqrt{45} + \sqrt{20} + \sqrt{5}$

4177. The president of KITTENS University asked Betty and Darlene to make up sandwiches for everyone coming to university picnic.

   If Betty worked alone, she could do it in 5 hours. Together, they can do it in 4 hours. How long would it take Darlene, if she were working alone?

2630. Solve $4x^2 + 3x - 2 = 0$ by completing the square.

2892. Joe decided he was going to try to do some cooking. One Tuesday he cooked up a big batch of baloney sauce. It was 20% fat (by weight). On Wednesday he cooked up a batch of yam sauce with extra bacon grease. It was 60% fat (by weight).

   On Thursday he mixed the two sauces together and found that he had 100 pounds of Joe's Super Sauce that was 50% fat. How much baloney sauce had gone into the mixture?

Joe's Super Sauce

595. Graph $y = x^2 - 3$ for $-3 \le x \le 3$.

1685. Solve $\begin{cases} 2x - 5y = 4 \\ 6x + 5y = 32 \end{cases}$

498. Which is larger? 2^5 or 5^2

990. Factor $x^2 - 2x - 24$

1017. Factor $30x^2 - 55x - 50$

1203. Solve $\dfrac{3}{x-1} + \dfrac{1}{2} = x - 1$

1524. Solve $x^2 - 5x - 2 = 0$

1583. Express as a decimal 10^{-4}

1681. State the reflexive law of equality.

What does x see *reflected* in the mirror?

Chapter Eleven

First part: Problems on Each Topic

Functions, Domains, Codomains, Range, and Images

1527. A) Can the domain be any set?

B) Can the codomain be any set?

C) If you specify the domain and the codomain, have you specified the function?

869. Invent a function in which the domain is the set {A, B, C, D, . . . ,W, X, Y, Z} and the second set (the codomain) is the set of all the flavors of ice cream that were ever sold in Kansas in 2005.

993. Is this a function?

In case you would like to know: α, β, and γ (alpha, beta, and gamma) are the first three letters of the Greek alphabet.

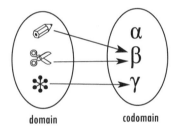

domain   codomain

1047. Is this a function?

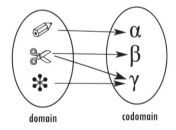

domain   codomain

1122. Is this a function?

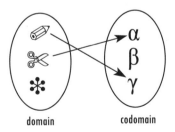

domain   codomain

644. What is the definition of the **range** of a function?

Chapter Eleven

1020. Suppose we have a function in which the domain and the codomain are the natural numbers ℕ.   (ℕ = {1, 2, 3, 4, 5, . . .}.)

Suppose the rule is: Assign to each element of the domain the number that is five larger than it. In symbols, assign to n, the number n + 5.

What is the range of this function?

1204. How many different functions could have a domain equal to ℕ and a codomain equal to {★}?   ℕ is the set of natural numbers {1, 2, 3, 4, 5, 6, 7, 8 . . .}.

1390. Let's play Guess the Function. Try to guess the rule that defines this function: Nevada → Neither   Washington → Pac Iowa → Neither   South Carolina → At   Argentina → At   Ireland → At   Kansas → Neither   California → Pac   Montana → Neither   Italy → Neither

(Hint: It may help to look at a map to guess the rule.)

Slope

1258. Consider the line that passes through (3, 7) and (8, 9).

    A) What is the change in y? (the rise)
    B) What is the change is x? (the run)
    C) What is the slope of this line?

5740. Is the slope of this line positive, negative or zero?

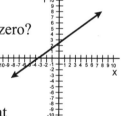

2894. Graph the line that passes through (1, −6) that has a slope of $\frac{9}{2}$

Slope-intercept Form of the Line $y = mx + b$

645. What is the slope of the line $y = 5x + 73$?

994. What is the slope of the line $4x + y = 12$?

1022. What is the slope of the line $3x + 7 = 2y$?

1205. What is the point at which the line $y = 32x + 55$ hits the y-axis?

1260. What is the point at which the line $y = 3.5x - 17$ hits the y-axis?

1391. What is the point at which the line $y + x = 50$ hits the x-axis? (Read carefully: the x-axis.)

Second part: the 𝔐ixed 𝔅ag: a variety of problems from this chapter and previous material

596. Solve $4x^2 = 3 - 16x$ by completing the square.

997. Graph $x = 7$

1208. Solve $4x^2 + 10 = 19$

1263. Is this a function?
The domain is $\{3, 5\}$ and the codomain is $\{L, M, N\}$ and the rule is the image of 3 is L and the image of 5 is L.

1411. Let the domain and codomain be the set $\mathbb{N}$. ($\mathbb{N}$ is the set of natural numbers $\{1, 2, 3, 4, 5, \ldots\}$.)

Consider the function defined by the rule: Assign to each number n in the domain, the number n^2 in the codomain.

What is the range of this function?

646. Simplify $\sqrt[3]{-64}$

597. e is an irrational number that you will encounter for the first time in advanced algebra. e will be used frequently in calculus.
It is approximately equal to 2.71828182845904523536028747113527.

One of the official definitions of e is the number that when you plot the curve $y = e^x$, you find that the slope of $y = e^x$ at the point x is equal to y. Clear? Probably not.

Another neat definition of e is the value of $(1 + \dfrac{1}{n})^n$ when n becomes infinitely large. Clear? Probably not.

So, for the time being, let's ignore the two definitions of e. All you are given is that e is an irrational number.

Your job is to give an argument that 5e must also be irrational.

2634. Express 38/233 as a ratio.

3555. Express $0.8383838383\ldots$ as a fraction.

3170. If the radius of a circle is 6 cm, what is the exact circumference of the circle?

2104. Name a number that is a whole number, that is not a natural number.

2108. Solve $\dfrac{7}{3x} - 6x = 5$

2302. Solve $4x^2 + x = 6$

2522. Simplify $\sqrt{6} + \sqrt{54} + \sqrt{8}$

598. Are these two sets equal: {a, b, c} and {b, a, c}?

1024. In a right triangle, the hypotenuse is equal to 20, and one leg is equal to 10. What is the length of the other leg? Simplify your answer (but do not approximate it).

1212. Simplify by rationalizing the denominator. $\dfrac{\sqrt{x} + 4}{\sqrt{x}}$

2121. $\dfrac{\dfrac{x+2}{x+6} - \dfrac{x+8}{x^2+4x-12}}{\dfrac{x^2+11x-8}{x^2+9x-22} - \dfrac{x-1}{x-2}}$

648. Simplify $8^{1/2}$

1125. By the symmetric law of equality, what does $\pi = \dfrac{C}{d}$ become?

277. Solve $x/3 = \sqrt{x-2}$

599. Factor $5x^2 + 31x + 6$

1130. To celebrate National Seafood Month, Joe went down to the wholesale market and bought a truck load of fish.

He could clean all of those fish in 30 days. Darlene could clean them all in 20 days. How long would it take them to clean that truck load of fish if they worked together?

National Seafood
M·O·N·T·H

1265. Solve $9x - 44 = 2x + 44$

275. Is this a function?

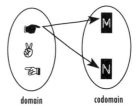

domain   codomain

1049. What is the slope of the line $5x - y = 45$?

1255. How many different functions could have a domain equal to {★} and a codomain equal to $\mathbb{N}$? $\mathbb{N}$ is the set of natural numbers {1, 2, 3, 4, 5, 6, 7, 8 . . .}.

1692. Fred worked for 3 hours hoeing weeds. A professional worked 4 times as fast as Fred and worked for 8 hours. Together they hoed 210 rows. How fast did Fred work?

    Your answer will be in rows/hour.

255. Graph the line that passes through (–4, 3) that has a slope of $\dfrac{-5}{8}$

2511. Consider the line that passes through (–5, 23) and (–3, –4).

    A) What is the change in y? (the rise)
    B) What is the change is x? (the run)
    C) What is the slope of this line?

258. How many different functions could have a domain equal to {♠, ☺} and range equal to {A, B, C}?

2072. Is the slope of this line positive, negative or zero?

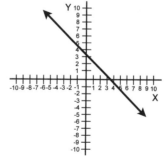

5114. Solve $6x^2 - 54 = 0$

Chapter Twelve

First part: Problems on Each Topic

Graphing Inequalities in Two Dimensions

2527. Graph y = (4/3)x – 3

3022. Graph y ≤ (4/3)x – 3

4180. Graph y < (4/3)x – 3

1050. Graph x ≥ 0

1136. Graph y ≥ 0

1529. Graph 2x – 3y < 12

1730. When Fred jogs for one minute, he burns 5 Calories. When he works out with weights, he burns 4 Calories each minute.

 If he wishes to burn at least 20 Calories, draw a graph of his possibilities. Let x be the number of minutes he jogs and y be the number of minutes he works out with weights.

1250. KITTENS University gave Fred 60¢ to spend for school supplies.

2 cents each

 Pencils cost 2¢ each. Pens cost 3¢ each. Let x equal the number of pencils he bought. Let y equal the number of pens he bought.

3 cents each

 Graph Fred's possibilities.

Division by Zero

1906. Multiple choice question. Which of the following does not make sense?

 A) Red, if one twirls yesterday frog.

 B) Division by zero.

 C) Neither of the above make any sense.

2444. Which is larger: $\dfrac{5}{1000}$ or $\dfrac{5}{0.001}$?

6924. This is a three-line proof that $\dfrac{7}{0}$ can't be a number.

I will give you the first two lines and you supply the last line.

Line 1: Every number when multiplied by zero gives a zero answer. If you multiply a million by zero, you get zero. If you multiply –80 by zero, you get zero.

Line 2: If you multiply $\dfrac{7}{0}$ by zero, you get 7 as an answer.

Watch me do it. $\dfrac{7}{0} \times 0 = \dfrac{7}{\cancel{0}} \times \cancel{0} = 7$

Solving Linear Inequalities

2303. Solve $3x - 7 > x - 3$

2525. Solve $10x + 8 \leq 22x$

2635. Solve $-5x \geq 30$

2896. Solve $-16 \leq -x$

5099. Solve $-4x + 1.5 > x$

5608. Solve $6x - 11 > 6x + 3$

5454. Solve $82x - 71 < 82x + 1000$

Second part: the 𝔐ixed 𝔅ag: a variety of problems from this chapter and previous material

1241. Kingie uses 3 gallons of oil paint per hour when he's doing landscape paintings. Two gallons per hour when doing portraits. He only has 18 gallons of oil paint. Graph his possibilities. (Let x equal the number of hours he does landscapes and y, the number of hours he does portraits.)

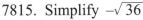

7815. Simplify $-\sqrt{36}$

8009. Simplify $\sqrt{90} + \sqrt{50} + \sqrt{160}$

1030. Suppose the domain and codomain are both $\mathbb{N}$. ($\mathbb{N}$ is the set of natural number $\{1, 2, 3, 4, 5, 6, \ldots\}$.)

Suppose the rule is: Assign to each number n in the domain, the number $n - 4$.

Explain why this is not a function.

2304. Graph y = 10x for –5 ≤ x ≤ 5

You may want to use different scales for the x- and y-axes.

5104. Solve $\begin{cases} 3x + y = 26 \\ 7x - 2y = 39 \end{cases}$

6117. What is the slope of the line 66 = 3x – 5y?

5812. Solve $0 = 3x^2 + 9x - 5$ by completing the square.

6955. Which of these are functions?

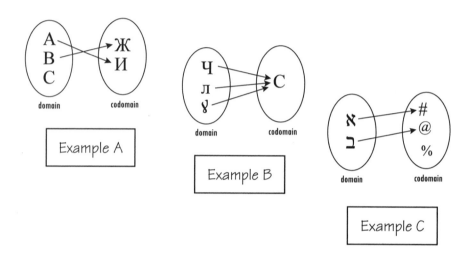

8212. What is the index of $\sqrt{34vwxyz}$?

5816. Solve 6y + 38 + 4y = 68

7333. Darlene bought a new fondue pot. She filled it with melted chocolate and set out a bowl of giant strawberries to dip in the chocolate.

Joe ate the chocolate strawberries three times as fast as Darlene. In 6 minutes, they had consumed 12 strawberries. How fast was Darlene eating them?

9130. What are "{" and "}" called?

1244. Simplify $\dfrac{x^9 - y^{-9}}{y^{-10}}$

8952. Express as a fraction 0.907907907907. . . .

1140. Is it possible for a function to have a finite domain (translation: a set with a finite number of elements in it) and an infinite codomain (translation: a set with an infinite number of elements in it)?

5022. $x + 1\overline{)x^3 + 1}$

1420. He can build a brick wall in 18 hours. Working with his son, they can build that wall in 12 hours. How long would it take his son to build the wall if he worked alone?

3030. Solve $\sqrt{6 - y} + y = 0$

6511. Solve $6x^2 + 4x + 3 = 0$

1220. Simplify by rationalizing the denominator.

$$\frac{a}{\sqrt{a} + b}$$

2539. $\dfrac{\dfrac{4}{y - 2} + \dfrac{y^2 + 6y + 41}{y^2 - 7y + 10}}{\dfrac{y^2 + 6y + 11}{y^2 + 4y - 12} + \dfrac{2}{y + 6}}$

6532. Factor $7x^2 - 63$

6333. This is an actual photograph of Joe's living room. Darlene took a handful of dust off the television—it was 35% lint—and mixed it with a handful of dust off the chair—it was 75% lint.

   She held 12 grams of Joe's dust that was 45% lint. How many grams had she taken off the television?

Joe's Living Room

7791. Suppose that a and b are natural numbers, and a < b. (The set of natural numbers = {1, 2, 3, 4, 5, 6, . . .}.)

   Is it possible to find values for a and b such that $a^b < b^a$?

20. $6x^2y + 55\xi = 6x^2y + 55\xi$ is an example of the reflexive property of equality. Anything is always equal to itself.

It can be as simple as $b = b$ or as complicated as
$3\sqrt{tyz} + 3.14d + \log_8 4.1 + \xi^{55} = 3\sqrt{tyz} + 3.14d + \log_8 4.1 + \xi^{55}$.

22. Your three examples of the commutative law of multiplication will probably be different than mine:

$$35 \times 77 = 77 \times 35$$
$$4 \times 8 = 8 \times 4$$
$$\pi \times 0.39872 = 0.39872 \times \pi$$

37. The empty set { } is the set that contains zero elements. It is finite. It wouldn't take much time at all to count all of the elements in the empty set.

Infinite sets are those sets that you could never finish counting even if you had an unlimited amount of time. They go on forever.

39. It takes three hours for every two pages of Life of Fred that I write. The ratio of hours to pages is 3:2 which means $3 \div 2$ or $\dfrac{3}{2}$

45. {me, you} is a set with two elements in it. So is $\{7, \pi\}$. There are many different answers. The "curly" parentheses "{" and "}" are called braces.

Parentheses: ( )
Braces: { }
Brackets: [ ]

51. $x^{20}x^3 = x^{23}$ by the rule $x^m x^n = x^{m+n}$
In this particular problem: $x^{20}x^3 =$
(xxxxxxxxxxxxxxxxxxxx)(xxx) = xxxxxxxxxxxxxxxxxxxxxxx = x^{23}

53. {☎, ✈} and {☺, ✿} both have two members, but they are not equal. Two sets are equal if they have the same members, not just the same number of members.

The Complete Solutions and Answers

58. $-25 + (-77) + 30 = -102 + 30 = -72$

71. If two sets are equal they must have exactly the same members. If they have exactly the same members, then they must have exactly the same number of elements in each set. So two sets with different numbers of members cannot be equal.

123. The set of all words in the English language is finite. The average English speakers active speaking vocabulary is usually estimated between 15,000 and 30,000 words. The number of words that the average person can recognize or understand is about 100,000. Most college dictionaries have about 150,000 entries.

I keep a college dictionary near every spot in the house that I do reading: the window seat, the recliner in the family room, in the cave room (no windows) where I read things from the Internet, and my bed.

I keep my "big" dictionary beside the recliner in the family room, because that's the place I read books with the most difficult vocabulary. This dictionary comes in three volumes and contains a little over 450,000 words. That is a finite number.

That is a lot less than a million: 1,000,000.

That is a lot less than a billion: 1,000,000,000.

154. 7/33 as a ratio is 7:33.

187. The set of whole numbers is {0, 1, 2, 3, . . .}.
The set of natural numbers is {1, 2, 3, . . . }.
Two sets are equal if they contain the same members. The set of whole numbers contains the element 0, but the set of natural numbers does not contain 0. Therefore the two sets are not equal.

188. $52 + (-13) + 10 + (-13) = 36$ (or +36)

First, add up all of the positive numbers, which in this case are 52 and 10, and get 62.

Second, add up all of the negative numbers, which in this case are -13 and -13, and get -26.

Finally, add the 62 and the -26 to get 36. $62 + (-26) = 36$

The Complete Solutions and Answers

200. Since every natural number {1, 2, 3, 4, . . . } is an integer {. . . –3, –2, –1, 0, 1, 2, 3, . . .} it is not possible to name a natural number that is not an integer. In later mathematics, we will say that the natural numbers are a subset of the integers.

201. We need to ship 600 cars to Freedonia, and the order specifies that 28% of those cars should have tape players.
    40% of the older cars have tape players, and 15% of the newer cars do. How many older cars should we ship?

❶ Using the Let x = . . . approach:

Let x = the number of older cars we ship.

Then 600 – x = the number of newer cars we ship.

Then 0.4x = the number of tape players in the older cars.

Then 0.15(600 – x) = the number of tape players in the newer cars.

Finally, since they want 168 tape players (28% of 600), we have the equation:

$$0.4x + 0.15(600 - x) = 168$$

$0.4x + 90 - 0.15x = 168$	distributive law
$0.25x + 90 = 168$	adding
$0.25x = 78$	subtracting 90 from both sides
$x = 312$	dividing both sides by 0.25

We should ship 312 of the older cars.

❷ Using the Six Pretty boxes approach:

	number of tape players	percent containing tape players	number of cars
older cars	0.4x	40%	x
newer cars	0.15(600 – x)	15%	600 – x

204. If we know that $7\xi = \sqrt{5}$, the symmetric law of equality allows us to say that $\sqrt{5} = 7\xi$.

The symmetric law of equality states that if a = b, then it must be true that b = a.

205. $44 \div 7$ as a ratio is 44:7.

The Complete Solutions and Answers

207. Going from 6 to –5, means $-5 - (+6) = -5 + (-6) = -11$.

... -10 -9 -8 -7 -6 -5 -4 -3 -2 -1 0 1 2 3 4 5 6 7 8 9 10 ...

-11 indicates that I went 11 units to the left.

208. $y = 3x - 2$ is a linear equation. Its graph will be a line. We need to find two points on the graph, and then we can draw the line.

To find a point on the graph takes two steps: (1) name any value for x; and (2) find the corresponding value for y.

Suppose $x = 2$. Then $y = 3x - 2$ becomes $y = 3(2) - 2$, which is 4. So (2, 4) is on the line.

Suppose $x = -1$. Then $y = 3x - 2$ becomes $y = 3(-1) - 2$, which is –5. So (–1, –5) is on the line.

We plot those two points and draw the line.

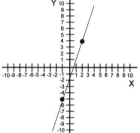

221. Your answer may differ from mine. One possibility is {4, #, Ulysses, π}. Another possibility is {Millard, ball, loaf, Colorado}.
(Millard Fillmore was the 13th President. Ulysses S. Grant was the 18th President.)

240. $(-8) + (-8) + (-8) + 3 = -21$

First, you add up all the positive numbers, which in this case is just +3, and get +3.

Second, add up all the negative numbers, which in this case are –8, –8, and –8, and get –24.

Finally, you combine the 3 and the –24 and get –21.

243. $55 + 23 = 23 + 55$ is not an example of the commutative law of multiplication because it isn't multiplication. (However, it is an example of the commutative law of addition.)

245. The cardinality of {8.29872} is 1. The set has one member.

The Complete Solutions and Answers

248. Simplify by rationalizing the denominator $\dfrac{4x}{\sqrt{5x}}$

Multiply top and bottom by $\sqrt{5x}$
$$= \frac{4x\sqrt{5x}}{\sqrt{5x}\,\sqrt{5x}}$$

$$= \frac{4x\sqrt{5x}}{5x}$$

251. $x - 1\overline{)\,x^4 - 1\,}$

Add in the missing terms and divide.

$$
\begin{array}{r}
x^3 + x^2 + x\ \ + 1 \\
x - 1\overline{)\,x^4 + 0x^3 + 0x^2 + 0x - 1\,} \\
\underline{x^4 - x^3} \\
x^3 + 0x^2 \\
\underline{x^3 - x^2} \\
x^2 + 0x \\
\underline{x^2 - x} \\
x - 1 \\
\underline{x - 1} \\
0
\end{array}
$$

$x - 1$ divides evenly into $x^4 - 1$ since there is no remainder.

Therefore, we can say that

$$(x - 1)(x^3 + x^2 + x + 1) = x^4 - 1.$$

This is true for the same reason as $2\overline{)\,14\,}^{\,7}$ implies $2 \times 7 = 14$.

255. Graph the line that passes through $(-4, 3)$ that has a slope of $\dfrac{-5}{8}$

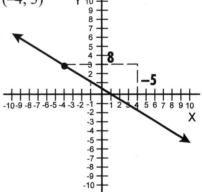

258. There are no possible functions with a domain equal to {☻, ☺} and range equal to {A, B, C}. The range of a function is the set of images. ☻ will have one image, say, A, and ☺ will have one image, say, B. Then nothing would "hit" C.

The Complete Solutions and Answers

275. Is this a function?

Each element in the domain must have exactly one image in the codomain.

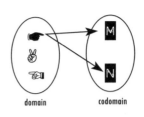

It's not a function since ☞ has two images.

You could also say it is not a function since ✌ has no image.

You could also say it is not a function since ✍ has no image.

     This really isn't a function!

277. $x/3 = \sqrt{x-2}$

First step is to isolate the radical.

This has already been done. $x/3 = \sqrt{x-2}$

Second step is to square both sides. $x^2/9 = x - 2$

To solve an equation containing fractions, the first
        step is to multiply through by 9. $x^2 = 9x - 18$

Solve the equation by factoring.

     Put everything on one side. $x^2 - 9x + 18 = 0$

     Factor. $(x - 6)(x - 3) = 0$

     Set each factor equal to zero. $x - 6 = 0$ OR $x - 3 = 0$

                             $x = 6$ OR $x = 3$

Check each answer in the original equation.

$x = 6$ $x = 3$

$6/3 \overset{?}{=} \sqrt{6-2}$ $3/3 \overset{?}{=} \sqrt{3-2}$

Yes   Yes

The final answer is $x = 6$ or $x = 3$.

300. $(2x - 6)(x - 8) = 2x^2 - 16x - 6x + 48 = 2x^2 - 22x + 48$

First the 2x times the x.

Then the 2x times the –8.

Then –6 times the x.

Then –6 times the –8.

303. $\sqrt[3]{-125} = -5$, since $(-5)^3 = -125$.

The Complete Solutions and Answers

317. It makes sense to talk about adding two numbers together. You can write 7 + 6, and we know the answer will be 13.

  Does it make sense to add a square to a circle? No.

  Does it make sense to add a bird and a house? No.

  It doesn't make any sense to add a set and a number together. {7} + 6 will not work.

  In fact, {7} + {6} also does not make any sense. The only things that we add together are two numbers.

326. 9 ÷ 5 as a ratio is 9:5.

333. $(+20) + (-7) + (+5) + (-4) = 14$ (or +14)

  To do this kind of problem add up all of the positive numbers, which in this case are +20 and +5, and get +25.

  Then add up all of the negative numbers, which in this case are –7 and –4, and get –11.

  Finally, combine the +25 and the –11 to get +14.

347. The whole numbers are {0, 1, 2, 3, 4, . . .}. The smallest possible whole number is 0.

351. $99x + 99y = 32$, can be replaced by

  $99(x + y) = 32$ because we know

that $99x + 99y$ is equal to $99(x + y)$ by the distributive property.

356. $-22 - (-3) = -22 + (+3) = -19$. Subtracting a negative number is the same as adding a positive number. A loss of 22 and a gain of 3 result in a net loss of 19.

358. Which kind of factoring should you always look for first? Common factoring. By taking out a common factor, it will often make the rest of the factoring much easier.

360. Is it possible to find a positive number w such that $w^2 < w$?

If $w \geq 1$, then it won't be true that $w^2 < w$. But if $0 < w < 1$, then it will always be true that $w^2 < w$. For example, if $w = \frac{1}{3}$ then $\frac{1}{9} < \frac{1}{3}$

The Complete Solutions and Answers

370. If a circle has a radius of 8 meters, its exact circumference is 16π meters. π does not equal $\frac{22}{7}$, nor does it equal 3.1416.

401. Set A is the set of all integers less than 5 and can be written as $\{\ldots -3, -2, -1, 0, 1, 2, 3, 4\}$. Set B is the set of all whole numbers less than 5 and can be written as $\{0, 1, 2, 3, 4\}$. A ≠ B since A contains, for example, the number −72 and B does not contain −72.

402. There is no such thing as the commutative law of subtraction. If there was such a law, then a − b = b − a would always be true. But, just to take one example, 55 − 3 does not equal 3 − 55.

405. The natural numbers $\{1, 2, 3, \ldots\}$ is an infinite set. It never ends. If you were given an unlimited amount of time, you could never count all of the natural numbers.

In Heaven you could easily count all of the atoms in the observable physical universe. As mentioned in the *Life of Fred: Beginning Algebra Expanded Edition*, there are approximately 10,000,000,000,000,000,000 000,000,000,000,000,000,000,000,000,000,000,000,000,000,000, 000,000,000 atoms in the observable universe. That is one followed by 79 zeros. And that number is much, much smaller than a googol (not to be confused with Google). A googol is one followed by 100 zeros. The word *googol* can be found in any good dictionary.

And for really big finite number, a googolplex is a one followed by a googol of zeros. Both *googol* and *googolplex* entered the English language somewhere between 1935 and 1940.

407. Factor $x^2 + 44x + 66x^5$. This is a test. The previous question asked what kind of factoring should you always look for first. The answer was common factoring.

There is a common factor of x in $x^2 + 44x + 66x^5$. $x^2 + 44x + 66x^5 = x(x + 44 + 66x^4)$. That is as far as you can factor it.

436. If some number times −83 is equal to a positive answer, that number must be negative. It can't be zero, since zero times −83 is zero. It can't be positive, since a positive number times −83 would give a negative answer.

The Complete Solutions and Answers

441. $-600 + 200 = -400$

443. Joe can make 2 pancakes/minute. After Joe had been making pancakes for 40 minutes, Darlene started making pancakes at the rate of 3 pancakes/minute. (Darlene was working on the left side of the stove and Joe on the right side.) How long would Darlene have to cook until she had made as many pancakes as Joe?

❶ Using the Let t = . . . approach:

     Let t = the number of minutes that Darlene would be cooking. (We start solving a word problem by letting the variable equal the thing we are trying to find out.)

     Then t + 40 = the number of minutes that Joe would be cooking. (He had a 40 minute head start.)

     Then 3t = the number of pancakes that Darlene would make. (She was making 3 pancakes/minute for t minutes.)

     Then 2(t + 40) = the number of pancakes that Joe would make. (He was making 2 pancakes/minute for t + 40 minutes.)

     Finally, since they would be making the same number of pancakes, we have the equation $\qquad 3t = 2(t + 40)$

Using the distributive law $\qquad 3t = 2t + 80$

Subtracting 2t from both sides $\qquad t = 80$

It would take Darlene 80 minutes to catch up with Joe.

❷ Using the Six Pretty Boxes approach:

	pancakes made	pancakes per minute	time
Darlene			t
Joe			

→

	pancakes made	pancakes per minute	time
Darlene			t
Joe			t + 40

	pancakes made	pancakes per minute	time
Darlene		3	t
Joe		2	t + 40

→

	pancakes made	pancakes per minute	time
Darlene	3t	3	t
Joe	2(t+40)	2	t + 40

445. Going from 4 to 11 means $11 - 4$ which is 7.

453. $5x = 37$ can become $37 = 5x$ by the symmetric law of equality.

The Complete Solutions and Answers

460. $-19 + 39 = 20$ This could also have been written as $-19 + 39 = +20$. The numbers 20 and +20 are the same number. This is like a loss of 19 followed by a gain of 39.

467. If I measure the time it takes me to grow my sunflowers in days and then measure that in weeks, the ratio of those two measurements is 7:1. For example, if it takes me 42 days, that is the same as 6 weeks, and the ratio 42:6 which means 42/6 which is the same as 7/1 which means 7:1.

470. $x = 2y + 1$ is a linear equation. We need to plot two points, and then we can draw the line.

    To graph a point, you name a value for either x or y and then compute the value for the other variable.

    In this case, it is easier to name values for y, and then find the corresponding values for x.

    For example, if I say that y is 3, then $x = 2y + 1$ becomes $x = 2(3) + 1$, which is 7. So (7, 3) is a point on the graph.

    If I say that y is –4, then $x = 2y + 1$ becomes $x = 2(-4) + 1$, which is –7. So (–7, –4) is a point on the graph.

    Plot those two points and draw the line.

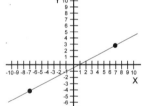

492. Your answers may be different than mine.
{1, 2, 3, 4, . . . } also known as the natural numbers.
{0, 1, 2, 3, . . . } also known as the whole numbers.
{5, 6, 7, 8, 9, 10, . . . } which is the set of natural numbers greater than four.
{1/2, 1/3, 1/4, 1/5, 1/6, . . . }
{. . . –3, –2, –1, 0, 1, 2, 3, 4, . . .} also known as the integers.
{1, 0.1, 0.001, 0.0001, 0.00001, . . . }
{2, 4, 6, 8, 10, 12, 14, . . .} also known as the even natural numbers.
{100, 200, 300, 400, 500, . . . }

494. Going from 38 to 32 means $32 - 38 = 32 - (+38)$ or $32 + (-38)$ which equals –6.

The Complete Solutions and Answers

495. Solve $6x^2 - 7x - 5 = 0$

It is already in the general form $ax^2 + bx + c = 0$.

We know that a = 6, b = –7, and c = –5.

We recite aloud the quadratic formula minus b, plus or minus the square root of b squared minus four a c, all over two a, and simply write out the final answer:

$$x = \frac{7 \pm \sqrt{49 - 4(6)(-5)}}{12}$$

The rest is just arithmetic:

$$x = \frac{7 \pm \sqrt{169}}{12}$$

Anybody who knows their 13 times tables recognizes that $13^2 = 169$, so we can simplify our answer a bit.

$$x = \frac{7 \pm 13}{12} \qquad x = 20/12 \text{ or } -6/12$$

$$x = \frac{5}{3} \text{ or } x = \frac{-1}{2}$$

A side note: Whenever the square root disappears and you just have regular fractions in your answer, that means that the original quadratic equation could have been solved by factoring.

Just for fun, let me solve it by factoring.

Start with $6x^2 - 7x - 5 = 0$

This is a "harder trinomial" in which the coefficient of the x^2 term is not equal to one. Using the "new quicker handy-dandy approach" from the textbook, I look for two expressions that multiply to $-30x^2$ and add $-7x$. That would be 3x and $-10x$.

So $6x^2 - 7x - 5$ splits into $6x^2 + 3x - 10x - 5$ which we then factor by grouping. $\quad 3x(2x + 1) - 5(2x + 1)$

$$(2x + 1)(3x - 5)$$

Set each factor equal to zero $\quad 2x + 1 = 0 \quad$ OR $\quad 3x - 5 = 0$

Solve for x $\qquad x = \frac{-1}{2}$ OR $x = \frac{5}{3}$

498. Which is larger? 2^5 or 5^2

$2^5 = 32 \qquad 5^2 = 25 \qquad 2^5 > 5^2$

The Complete Solutions and Answers

500. Two sets are equal if they contain exactly the same elements. So if you count the elements in one set and count the elements in the other set, you must come out with the same answer. {V, ξ, #} and {ξ, V, #} are two equal sets. The order in which you list the elements does not matter. These two sets each have three elements.

When you list the elements of a set inside braces, it is not permitted to list the same element twice. {A, α, 7, α} is a no-no.

501. The commutative law of division has about as much reality as ducks studying calculus. $\frac{2}{3}$ does not equal $\frac{3}{2}$

511. If I measure the length of my driveway in yards and then measure it in feet, the ratio of those two measurements is 1:3. There are fewer yards than there are feet. If my driveway were 5 yards long, then it would be 15 feet long. The ratio of yards to feet would be 5:15 which means 5/15 which equals 1/3 which means 1:3 when expressed as a ratio.

518. The integers are {. . . −3, −2, −1, 0, 1, 2, 3, 4, . . . }. The numbers on the left are smaller than the ones on the right.

 −1 is less than 0.
 −3 is less than −2.
 −100 is less than −40.
 −1,000,000 is less than −999,999.

Since the list goes on forever in both directions, it is not possible to name a smallest integer or a largest integer.

521. $99 - (-70) = 99 + (+70) = 169$ You change the two negative signs that are next to each other to plus signs.

522. Factor $x^2 + 13x + 22$. We want two numbers that add to 13 and multiply to 22. That would be +2 and +11.

We insert those numbers into (x   )(x   ) and get (x + 2)(x + 11).

523. To simplify $\sqrt{12}$ we use the rule $\sqrt{ab} = \sqrt{a}\sqrt{b}$. We want a to be a perfect square (such as 4, 9, 16, 25, 36, 49, 64 . . .).
$\sqrt{12} = \sqrt{4}\sqrt{3} = 2\sqrt{3}$.

The Complete Solutions and Answers

525. Darlene bought two copies of the novel *Gone With the Wind*. She suggested that each of them read it. Joe started reading his copy at the rate of 4 pages/hour. Five hours later Darlene starting reading at the rate of 14 pages/hour. How long will it take for Darlene to catch up to Joe?

❶ Using the Let t = . . . method.

Let t = the number of hours that Darlene read. (We start solving a word problem by letting t equal the thing we are trying to find out.)

Then t + 5 = the number of hours that Joe read. (Joe read 5 hours longer than Darlene.)

Then 14t = the number of pages that Darlene read. (Since she reads at the rate of 14 pages/hour and she read for t hours.)

Then 4(t + 5) = the number of pages that Joe read. (Since Joe reads at the rate of 4 pages/hour and read for t + 5 hours.)

Finally, 14t = 4(t + 5)   (Since they both read the same number of pages.)

Using the distributive property	$14t = 4t + 20$
Subtracting 4t from both sides	$10t = 20$
Dividing both sides by 10	$t = 2$

Darlene read for 2 hours before catching up with Joe.

(For fun, we check our answer. If Darlene read for 2 hours at the rate of 14 pages/hour, then she read 28 pages. Joe read for 5 hours more than Darlene. Joe read for 7 hours. If Joe read for 7 hours at the rate of 4 pages/hour, he read 28 pages. Both of them read 28 pages.)

❷ Using the Six Pretty Boxes approach.

	pages read	pages per hour	hours
Joe			
Darlene			t

→

	pages read	pages per hour	hours
Joe			t + 5
Darlene			t

←

	pages read	pages per hour	hours
Joe		4	t + 5
Darlene		14	t

→

	pages read	pages per hour	hours
Joe	4(t+5)	4	t + 5
Darlene	14t	14	t

527. $4(x + y) + 3x^6 = \pi d$

$4x + 4y + 3x^6 = \pi d$ distributive law

$\pi d = 4x + 4y + 3x^6$ symmetric law of equality

The Complete Solutions and Answers

530. In graphing the linear equation $2x + 3y = 6$, one nice trick is to name values of x that make the arithmetic easier.

If I let $x = 7$, then $2x + 3y = 6$ would become $2(7) + 3y = 6$.

$$14 + 3y = 6$$
$$3y = -8$$
$$y = \frac{-8}{3}$$

and I would be plotting $(7, \frac{-8}{3})$. ☹ Not a very nice pair of numbers.

Instead, if I let $x = 0$, then $2x + 3y = 6$ becomes $2(0) + 3y = 6$, which gives $y = 2$. I plot the point $(0, 2)$. ☺

If I let $y = 0$, then $2x + 3y = 6$ becomes $2x + 3(0) = 6$, which gives $x = 3$. I plot the point $(3, 0)$. ☺

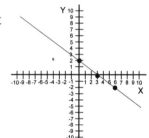

If I let $x = 6$, then $2x + 3y = 6$ becomes $2(6) + 3y = 6$, which gives $y = -2$. I plot the point $(6, -2)$. ☺

Special hint for extra success: It is so easy to make silly errors when plotting points. I do that all the time. When I plot a line, I usually plot three points instead of two. Then if the three points are not all in a straight line, I know I've made an error.

532. If I start at the top of Mt. Everest (29,028 feet above sea level) and walk down to the ocean and then dive 30 feet under the sea, this is the same as $-30 - (+29,028) = -30 + (-29,028)$ since subtracting a positive number is the same as adding its negative. It looks like you interchange the $-$ and the $+$ sign. $-30 + (-29,028) = -29,058$ feet.

540. An integer that is not a whole number is any element of the set $\{\ldots -4, -3, -2, -1\}$.

$-6\frac{1}{2}$ would not be correct because it is not an integer.

-100.13 would not be correct because it is not an integer.

963 would not be correct because it *is* a whole number.

541. If you bake a pizza and then eat it, you are happy. If you eat it and then bake it, your stomach may be very unhappy. The two acts are not commutative.

The Complete Solutions and Answers

544. Factor $y^2 + 10y + 25$. We want two numbers that add to 10 and multiply to 25. That would be +5 and +5.

We insert them into (y   )(y   ) and get $(y + 5)(y + 5)$.

547. Factor $20y^2 - 39y + 18$

We want to find two things that add to –39y and multiply to $360y^2$ (where $360y^2$ is $(20y^2)(18)$.)

We try –12y and –30y. They add to –42y.

We try –6y and –60y. They add to –66y. We're going in the wrong direction. We want the sum to be –39y. The two things have to be closer to each other than –12y and –30y.

We try –20y and –18y. They add to –38y.

We try –24y and – 15y. They add to –39y. ☺

$20y^2 - 39y + 18$ becomes

$20y^2 - 24y - 15y + 18$ which we will now factor by grouping.

$4y(5y - 6) - 3(5y - 6)$

$(5y - 6)(4y - 3)$

560. Nothing in the physical universe is infinite, not even the number of dollar bills that the government could print.

You can't go out walking in the forest, or in Wal-Mart, or among the stars and hope to see a set with an infinite number of members of it. If you want to find an infinite set, one good place to look is in the world of thought.

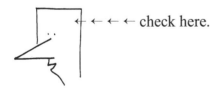 ← ← ← check here.

585. $30 - (+40) = 30 + (-40) = -10$ To subtract a positive number is the same as adding a negative. If you had $30 and you lost $40, it could be written as $30 – ($40). On the other hand, if you had $30 and you acquired a debt of $40, it could be written as $30 + (–$40). In either case, your final net worth would be –$10.

The Complete Solutions and Answers

589. 5.7 is not a natural number. Five is a natural number, and so is six.

590. Joe got a sling shot for his birthday. In order to be safe, Joe would only shoot marshmallows. Standing right next to her, he asked Darlene to throw her teddy bear up into the air, which she did at 21 ft/sec.

Two seconds later, Joe fired a marshmallow at the bear at 105 ft/sec. How long did it take the marshmallow to hit the bear?

❶ Using the Let t = approach:

Let t = the number of seconds it took for the marshmallow to hit the bear. (We let the variable equal the thing we are trying to find.)

Then $t + 2$ = the number of seconds the bear was in the air before it was hit. (The bear was thrown upwards two seconds before the marshmallow was launched.)

Then $105t$ = the number of feet that the marshmallow traveled. (It went 105 ft/sec for t seconds.)

Then $21(t + 2)$ = the number of feet that the bear traveled before it was hit by the marshmallow. (It went 21 ft/sec for t + 2 seconds.)

Finally, since they both went the same distance, we get the equation

$$105t = 21(t + 2)$$
$$105t = 21t + 42 \qquad \text{the distributive law}$$
$$84t = 42 \qquad \text{subtract 21t from both sides}$$
$$t = \frac{42}{84} \qquad \text{divide both sides by 84}$$

The marshmallow went $\frac{1}{2}$ second.   ($\frac{42}{84}$ reduces to $\frac{1}{2}$)

❷ Using the Six Pretty Boxes approach:

	d	r	t
Darlene			
Joe			t

→

	d	r	t
Darlene			t + 2
Joe			t

	d	r	t
Darlene		21	t + 2
Joe		105	t

→

	d	r	t
Darlene	21(t+2)	21	t + 2
Joe	105t	105	t

593. If we go from 55° down to –8°, that is the same as –8 – (+55) which equals –8 + (–55) = –63. Subtracting a positive number is the same as adding its negative.

The Complete Solutions and Answers

594. Solve $2x^2 + 5x + 1 = 0$

The general form for a quadratic equation is $ax^2 + bx + c = 0$

$2x^2 + 5x + 1 = 0$ is in the general form.

We can say that a = 2, b = 5, and c = 1.

This is the quadratic formula: $x = \dfrac{-b \pm \sqrt{b^2 - 4ac}}{2a}$

All we have to do is stuff a = 2, b = 5, and c = 1 into that formula and we are done.

THE HaRd Way to do that is to look at the formula and copy it, replacing each a by 2, each b by 5, and each c by 1. Your eyes go cRazy looking back at the formula.

THE easier Way is to memorize the formula. As you recite it, you just write out the answer. The words that you say to yourself are: Minus b, plus or minus the square root of b squared minus four a c, all over two a.

After you've done a half dozen of these, it will start to become automatic. You will be able to solve quadratic equations as fast as you can write them.

If someone asks you, "In what month does spring officially start?" you will respond, "March and minus b, plus or minus the square root of b squared minus four a c, all over two a."

If someone asks you, "What do you call your father?" you will respond, "Dad and minus b, plus or minus the square root of b squared minus four a c, all over two a."

To solve $2x^2 + 5x + 1 = 0$ in a single step:

$$x = \frac{-5 \pm \sqrt{25 - (4)(2)(1)}}{4}$$

which simplifies to $\qquad x = \dfrac{-5 \pm \sqrt{17}}{4}$

595. Graph $y = x^2 - 3$

If x = 0, then y = –3   plot (0, –3)

If x = 1, then y = –2   plot (1, –2)   also (–1, –2)

If x = ±2, then y = 1   plot (2, 1) and (–2, 1)

If x = ±3, then y = 6   plot (3, 6) and (–3, 6)

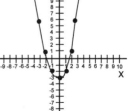

The Complete Solutions and Answers

596. Solve $4x^2 = 3 - 16x$

Put the x-terms on one side and the
   number on the other. $\qquad 4x^2 + 16x = 3$

Divide through by 4 to make the coefficient
   of the x^2 term equal to 1. $\qquad x^2 + 4x = \dfrac{3}{4}$

Complete the square. Half of 4 is 2, and
   2 squared is 4. $\qquad x^2 + 4x + 4 = \dfrac{3}{4} + 4$

Factor the left side and do the
   arithmetic on the right side. $\qquad (x + 2)^2 = \dfrac{19}{4}$

Take the square root of each side and
   add a ±. $\qquad x + 2 = \pm \dfrac{\sqrt{19}}{2}$

Transpose the 2. $\qquad x = -2 \pm \dfrac{\sqrt{19}}{2}$

597. 5e must be either rational or irrational.
Assume for a moment that it's rational. (We will look for a contradiction.)

   If 5e is rational, then it must equal a/b where a and b are integers
and b ≠ 0 because that is the definition of rational.

   If 5e = a/b, then e = a/5b (by algebra).

   Then e must rational (since it is equal to a fraction where the
numerator and the denominator are integers).

   But this contradicts the fact that e is irrational.

   Therefore, our assumption that 5e is rational must be wrong.

   Hence, 5e must be irrational.

598. Two sets are equal if they have the same members. It doesn't matter
what order they are listed in. {a, b, c} = {b, a, c}

599. Factor $5x^2 + 31x + 6$

This is one of the harder trinomials (of the form $ax^2 + bx + c$ where a ≠ 1)
We are looking for two expressions that multiply to $30x^2$ $\qquad$ $(5x^2)(6)$
and that add to 31x.

   That would be 30x and x.

We break $5x^2 + 31x + 6$ into $5x^2 + 30x + x + 6$ and factor by grouping.

$\qquad 5x^2 + 30x + x + 6 = 5x(x + 6) + (x + 6) = (x + 6)(5x + 1)$

The Complete Solutions and Answers

600. $\{1, 2, 3\} \cup \{3, 2, 1\} = \{1, 2, 3\}$

      The order in which you list the elements of a set is up to you. The set $\{1, 2, 3\}$ is the same as the set $\{3, 2, 1\}$. The only rule is that you do not repeat an element twice. $\{1, 2, 3, 1\}$ is not considered proper.

616. $-7 + (-8) = -15$ This is like a loss of seven followed by a loss of eight. The result is a loss of 15. If your football team loses seven yards on the first play and eight yards on the second play, the result is a total loss of 15 yards.

619. For every soda you buy, you get three straws. The ratio is 1:3. This means $1 \div 3$ or $\frac{1}{3}$.

624. Using braces, an example of an infinite set that contains the planet Neptune might be $\{\oplus, D, \text{Neptune}, 1, 2, 3, 4, \ldots\}$ or it might be $\{\text{Й}, \text{ж}, \bar{\omega}, \text{Neptune}, 2, 4, 6, 8, 10, \ldots\}$. Your answer may differ from mine.

629. The rational numbers may be defined as the set $\{\, x \mid x = a/b \text{ where } a$ and b are integers and $b \neq 0\}$.

      In English, the rational numbers are numbers *that can be expressed as a fraction* where the numerator is any integer and the denominator is any non-zero integer.

      So 7 is a rational number since it can be written as $\frac{7}{1}$.

      And 0.29 is a rational number since it can be written as $\frac{29}{100}$.

      π is not a rational number.

      $\sqrt{2}$ is not a rational number.

635. In *Life of Fred: Beginning Algebra Expanded Edition* we read that nothing in the physical universe is infinite. Even the number of atoms is finite. And there are a lot of atoms in each grain of sand.

640. $-40 + 8 = -32$ This problem is the same as $-40 + (+8)$. This is like a loss of 40 and a gain of eight. The result is the same as a loss of 32. You are in debt to $40 and you pay eight dollars, your debt is now only $32.

The Complete Solutions and Answers

642. $x^2 - 4 \overline{)x^4 - 16}$

Put in the missing terms, both in the divisor and the dividend.

$x^2 + 0x - 4 \overline{)x^4 + 0x^3 + 0x^2 + 0x - 16}$

$$\begin{array}{r} 8 \\ 5\overline{)40} \end{array}$$

5 is the divisor
40 is the dividend
8 is the quotient ("KWO-shent")

And then do the division.

$$\begin{array}{r}
x^2 \qquad + \quad 4 \\
x^2 + 0x - 4 \overline{)\, x^4 + 0x^3 + 0x^2 + 0x \; - 16} \\
\underline{x^4 + 0x^3 - 4x^2 \qquad\qquad} \\
4x^2 + 0x - 16 \\
\underline{4x^2 + 0x - 16}
\end{array}$$

Since it divided in evenly, with no remainer,
we can state that $(x^2 - 4)(x^2 + 4) = x^4 - 16$.

644. The **range** of a function is the set of those elements of the codomain that are the image of at least one element of the domain.

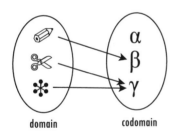

domain   codomain

For example, in this function, the range would be $\{\beta, \gamma\}$.

645. The slope of the line $y = 5x + 73$ is 5
$y = 5x + 73$ is in the $y = mx + b$ form so $m = 5$.

646. $\sqrt[3]{-64} = -4$ since $(-4)^3 = -64$.

648. $8^{1/2} = \sqrt{8} = \sqrt{4}\sqrt{2} = 2\sqrt{2}$

650. Does $\frac{22}{7}$ equal π? It couldn't. $\frac{22}{7}$ is a rational number. (It is in the form a/b where a and b are integers and $b \neq 0$.)

But π is irrational. Therefore $\frac{22}{7} \neq \pi$.

The Complete Solutions and Answers

651. $+48, -60, -3, -8$, and $+17$ is $+48 + (-60) + (-3) + (-8) + (+17)$.
　　　First, we add up the gains of 48 and 17 and get 65.
　　　Second, we add up the losses of $-60, -3$, and -8 and get -71.
　　　Last, we combine $+65 + (-71)$ and get -6 as the total for the week.

655. $8 - (+5) = 3$　(or $+3$)　This is "regular" subtraction that you
learned in arithmetic.

$$\begin{array}{r} 8 \\ -\ 5 \\ \hline 3 \end{array}$$

667. I don't think any movie stars ate 18 pounds of spaghetti for breakfast
yesterday. So the answer would be { }.

680. Darlene is one year older than Joe. If Darlene is x years old, then Joe
is $x - 1$ years old.

682. $1000 - (-25) = 1000 + (+25) = 1025$. Subtracting a negative
number is the same as adding a positive number. If you owed someone
$25 and they forgave your debt, that would have the same effect on your
net worth as if you found $25 on the street.

685. If we go from $-7°$ to $+40°$, that is $+40 - (-7) = 40 + (+7) = 47$.
Subtracting a negative number is the same as adding its positive.

699. {], (}　You can put almost anything into a set. Some sets can
contain just numbers, for example $\{3, 5, 9987, \frac{1}{2}\}$. A set can contain

musical symbols: $\{\flat, \natural, \sharp, \text{♪}, \text{♫}\}$. A set can contain concepts from

philosophy: {Truth, Justice, Goodness}.
　　　This is the empty set, { }, which contains nothing.
　　　This is the set that contains the empty set { { } }. Very strange.

711. Every whole number is a rational number. 43 can be written as $\frac{43}{1}$

and zero is a rational number because it can be written as $\frac{0}{4}$ (or as $\frac{0}{9}$ or

as $\frac{0}{-2}$ or as $\frac{0}{508922}$).

The Complete Solutions and Answers

714. $30 + (-10) = 20$ This is like a gain of 30 and loss of 10. The result is the same as a gain of 20.

718. For every soda you buy, you get three straws. The ratio of straws to sodas to 3:1 which means $3 \div 1$ or $\frac{3}{1}$

726. The largest negative integer is -1. This is the set of negative integers: $\{\ldots -4, -3, -2, -1\}$ and -1 is the largest of these.

729. $66 - (+88) = 66 + (-88) = -22$ Subtracting a positive number is the same as adding its negative. If the temperature goes up $66°$ on one day and goes down $88°$ on the next day, then the change over the two days is $-22°$.

732. If your net worth was $-\$500$ in January and it was $\$800$ in March, that is the same as $800 - (-500) = 800 + (+500) = \$1,300$. You gained $\$1,300$. Two negative signs together are the same as two plus signs.

740.
$$9y - 36 = 6y$$
Add 36 to both sides $\qquad 9y = 6y + 36$
Subtract 6y from both sides $\qquad 3y = 36$
Divide both sides by 3 $\qquad y = 12$

742. $14 - (-3) = 17$ The rule is that when you subtract a negative number it is the same as adding the positive number. You change the two negative signs that are next to each other to plus signs.
$14 - (-3)$ becomes $14 + (+3)$

790. Most rational numbers are not natural numbers. The natural numbers are $\{1, 2, 3, 4, 5, 6, \ldots \}$.
None of these are natural numbers: $\frac{1}{2}, \frac{2}{3}, \frac{7}{8}, \frac{11}{100}$.

800. $\{ \ \} \cup \{\text{☺}\} = \{\text{☺}\}$
$\{ \ \}$ is called the empty set or the null set.
The union of the empty set with any other set is equal to that other set.

The Complete Solutions and Answers

805. $6! = 6 \times 5 \times 4 \times 3 \times 2 \times 1 = 720$

807. Factor $w^2 + 15w + 56$. We want two numbers that add to 15 and multiply to 56. Here is where it really helps to know your multiplication tables. The numbers are +7 and +8. The answer is $(w + 7)(w + 8)$. It is okay if you wrote, instead, $(w + 8)(w + 7)$. The commutative law of multiplication is true: $ab = ba$.

810. $C = \pi d$ where C is circumference and d is diameter. Therefore $\frac{C}{\pi} = d$. Putting in the numbers: $\frac{44}{\frac{22}{7}} = d$.

$$44 \div \frac{22}{7} = \frac{44}{1} \times \frac{7}{22} = \frac{\overset{2}{\cancel{44}}}{1} \times \frac{7}{\underset{1}{\cancel{22}}} = 14 \text{ inches.}$$

838. The whole numbers are $\{0, 1, 2, 3, 4, \dots\}$. None of these are whole numbers: ½, 0.3, 5%, π, –3, doughnuts, my aunt.

840. $8 - 500 = 8 - (+500) = 8 + (-500)$ Subtracting a positive number is the same as adding its negative. A gain of 8 and a loss of 500 results in a net loss of 492. $8 + (-500) = -492$

845. If oil costs $121 a barrel, the ratio of barrels to dollars is 1:121. (If I had asked for the ratio of dollars to barrels, it would have been 121:1.)

852. For every four pepperoni pizzas that PieOne sells, it sells three combination pizzas. The ratio of pepperoni pizzas to combination pizzas is 4:3, which means $4 \div 3$ or $\frac{4}{3}$

855. $7 + (-4) = 3$ This is like a gain of seven and a loss of four. The result is the same as a gain of three.

864. Going from –5 to +5 means $+5 - (-5) = 5 + (+5) = 10$. If it is five degrees below zero (–5°) and it warms up to five degrees above zero (+5°), then the temperature has risen 10 degrees.

The Complete Solutions and Answers

866. $10 + (-11) - (-40) = 10 + (-11) + (+40)$ Subtracting a negative number is the same as adding a positive number.

      Then we add the positive numbers together: 10 and $40 = +50$.
We combine that with the -11 to get $+39$.

867. $\sqrt[3]{1000} = 10$, since $10^3 = 1000$

868.
$$\cfrac{\dfrac{2}{x^2 - x - 6} - \dfrac{5}{x^2 - 7x + 12} + \dfrac{6x^2 - 39x + 90}{(x+2)(x-3)(x-4)}}{\dfrac{5}{x^2 - x - 6} + \dfrac{2x-1}{(x^2 - 2x - 8)(x-3)}}$$

① Factor all the baby denominators.

$$\cfrac{\dfrac{2}{(x-3)(x+2)} - \dfrac{5}{(x-3)(x-4)} + \dfrac{6x^2 - 39x + 90}{(x+2)(x-3)(x-4)}}{\dfrac{5}{(x+2)(x-3)} + \dfrac{2x-1}{(x+2)(x-4)(x-3)}}$$

② The least common multiple of all the baby denominators is $(x - 3)(x - 4)(x + 2)$. Multiply each term by that and cancel.

$$\frac{2(x-4) - 5(x+2) + 6x^2 - 39x + 90}{5(x-4) + 2x - 1}$$

Combine together the top and combine together the bottom.

$$\frac{6x^2 - 42x + 72}{7x - 21} = \frac{6(x^2 - 7x + 12)}{7(x-3)} = \frac{6(x-3)(x-4)}{7(x-3)} = \frac{6(x-4)}{7}$$

869. Suppose the first set (the domain) is the set {A, B, C, D, . . . ,W, X, Y, Z} and the second set (the codomain) is the set of all the flavors of ice cream that were ever sold in Kansas in 2005.
Your answer may differ from mine.
✓ My first thought. Assign A and B to chocolate and all the rest to vanilla.
✓ My second thought. Assign all the letters to peach ice cream.

The Complete Solutions and Answers

870. $3 + 4 \cdot 6 / 12 / 3$

   $= \; 3 + 24 / 12 / 3$

   $= \; 3 + \; 2 / 3$

   $= \; 3 + \tfrac{2}{3}$

   $= \; 3\tfrac{2}{3}$

871. 34! means $34 \times 33 \times 32 \times 31 \times \ldots \times 2 \times 1$

     which is $34 \times 33!$

So 34! is 34 times larger than 33!

873. Factor $x^2 + 3x - 54$. We want two numbers that add to 3 and multiply to –54. Since they are multiplying to a negative number, one of them must be positive and one of them must be negative.

    Again, it really helps to know your multiplication tables.
The numbers are +9 and –6. The answer is $(x + 9)(x - 6)$.
Or $(x - 6)(x + 9)$, if you prefer.

875. Joe likes to draw with crayons. He can use up a whole box of crayons in 6 hours. Darlene likes to use crayons to fill out coupons in her bridal magazines. She can use up a whole box in 3 hours.

    Working together, how long would it take them to use up a whole box of crayons?

Let x = the number of hours it would take them to use up a box.

Then $\dfrac{1}{x}$ = the fraction of the box they could use up in one hour.

Joe can use up $\dfrac{1}{6}$ of a box in one hour (since he can use up a whole box in 6 hours).

Darlene can use up $\dfrac{1}{3}$ of a box in one hour (since she can use up a whole box in 3 hours).

$$\frac{1}{6} + \frac{1}{3} = \frac{1}{x}$$

The least common denominator is 6x. All the denominators can divide evenly into 6x. We eliminate the denominators in this fractional equation by multiplying each term by 6x.

$$\frac{1(6x)}{6} + \frac{1(6x)}{3} = \frac{1(6x)}{x}$$

$$x + 2x = 6$$

$$3x = 6$$

$$x = 2$$

Together, they can finish off a whole box of crayons in 2 hours.

The Complete Solutions and Answers

888. {A, ✪} and {✪, A} are equal. Two sets are equal if they contain the same elements. It does not matter in which order the elements are listed.

891. $15 - (-17) - (+3) = 15 + (+17) + (-3) = +32 + (-3) = 29$ (or +29)

900. Your answer may be different than mine. Here are several possible answers that I thought of:
{1, 2, 3, . . . , 88}
{0, 1, 2, . . . , 87}
{a, b, c, . . . , x, y, z, A, B, C, . . . , X, Y, Z, 1, 2, 3, . . . , 35, 36}.
The set {88} is not correct. It contains only one element.

907. $18 - (-20) - (+7) + (-3) =$
$18 + (+20) + (-7) + (-3)$
   Adding up the positive numbers, 18 and 20, we get +38.
   Adding up the negative numbers, −7 and −3, we get −10.
   Combining +38 and −10, we get 28 (or +28).

913. $500 - (-800) = 500 + (+800) = 1,300$

917. If my checking account was overdrawn by $70 and after making a deposit it was $800, my account went from −$70 to +$800. This is the same as $800 - (-70) = 800 + (+70) = \$870$. My deposit was $870.
   The deposit of $870 first raised my account from −$70 to $0 and then from $0 to $800.

918.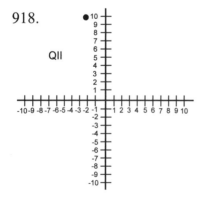

The point (−2, 10) is found by going two units to the left and 10 units upward.

It is in quadrant two, which is the upper-left quadrant.

The Complete Solutions and Answers

920. Joe and Darlene went into the hat decorating business. Joe decorated hats for 12 hours and Darlene decorated them for 9 hours. Darlene could decorate hats at a rate that was 10 hats/hour more than Joe's rate. They decorated the same number of hats. What was Joe's rate of decorating hats?

❶   Let r = the number of hats/hour that Joe could decorate.

Then r + 10 = the number of hats/hour that Darlene could do.

Then 12r = the number of hats Joe did. (He worked at the rate of r hats/hour for 12 hours.)

Then 9(r + 10) = the number that Darlene did.

Finally, since we know that they both decorated the same number of hats, we have the equation

$$12r = 9(r + 10)$$

distributive law	$12r = 9r + 90$
subtract 9r from both sides	$3r = 90$
divide both sides by 3	$r = 30$

Joe could decorate 30 hats/hour.

For fun, let's check to make sure that answer is correct.

If Joe did 30 hats/hour, then Darlene did 40 hats/hour since she worked at a rate that was 10 hats/hour more than Joe.

If Joe did 30 hats/hour and worked for 12 hours, he must have done 360 hats.

If Darlene did 40 hats/hour and worked for 9 hours, she must have done 360 hats. They each did 360 hats.

❷ Using Six Pretty Boxes

	hats done	hat/hour	hours
Joe		r	
Darlene			

→

	hats done	hat/hour	hours
Joe		r	
Darlene		r + 10	

	hats done	hat/hour	hours
Joe		r	12
Darlene		r + 10	9

→

	hats done	hat/hour	hours
Joe	12r	r	12
Darlene	9(r + 10)	r + 10	9

923. There are no people with eight eyes, so the set would be { }. This set is sometimes called the empty set or the null set.

The Complete Solutions and Answers

924. For any set A, it is always true that A ∪ { } = A.

For any number x, it is always true that x times 1 equals x.

{ } is called the identity element for union.

1 is called the identity element for multiplication.

For any number x, it is always true that $x + 0 = x$.

Zero is the identity element for addition.

Some people think of { } as Mr. Harmless when it comes to union of sets. No matter what set you start with, taking its union with { } will leave it unaffected: {325, ◖,☎,✏,ξ,℞} ∪ { } = {325, ◖,☎,✏,ξ,℞}.

Zero is Mr. Harmless when it comes to addition of numbers. No matter what number you start with, adding zero to it won't affect it.

929092399296611492⅓ + 0 = 929092399296611492⅓

925. $-6 - (+28) - (-9) + (-2) + (+7) =$

$-6 + (-28) + (+9) + (-2) + (+7)$ which changes everything to addition.

Then we combine the positive numbers, 9 and 7, to get +16.

Then we combine the negative numbers, –6, –28, and –2 to get –36.

A gain of 16 and a loss of 36 yields a loss of 20. $16 + (-36) = -20$

930. "{" and "}" are called braces.

941. There are many examples of a set that is easy to write in set builder notation, but is very difficult to write without set builder notation. Your answer will probably be different than mine.

Example #1: { x | x lives currently in San Francisco}. (It would be very difficult to list all those names.)

Example #2: { y | y is an ice cream flavor}. (It would be very hard to list them all.)

Example #3: { z | 4 < z < 5}. (Could you list all the numbers between 4 and 5? If you tried by writing {4.1, 4.12, $4\frac{1}{6}$, 4.34973, $4\frac{2}{3}$ } I bet you would leave out some numbers.

944. $15 + (-20) = -5$ This is like a gain of 15 and a loss of 20. The result is the same as a loss of five. On a football field if you gain 15 yards on one play and lose 20 yards on the next play, the result of the two plays is a net loss of five yards.

The Complete Solutions and Answers

948. $\{ y \mid$ y times y equals $-36 \}$ asks for the set of all numbers that when multiplied by themselves will equal -36.

> We know that every positive number times itself is positive.
>
> We know that every negative number times itself is positive.
>
> We know that zero times zero is zero.

Thus, there are no numbers that make $y^2 = -36$ true.

So $\{ y \mid$ y times y equals $-36 \}$ can be written as $\{ \ \}$, which is known as the empty set.

950. $\{ \ \} \cup \{x \mid x$ is an antelope$\} = \{x \mid x$ is an antelope$\}$.

Or you could write $\{ \ \} \cup \{x \mid x$ is an antelope$\} =$ the set of all antelopes.

951. Factor $24x^2 + 24x + 48$. It has been often said that the first kind of factoring that you always look for is a common factor.

> In this problem, the common factor is 24.
>
> $$24x^2 + 24x + 48 = 24(x^2 + x + 2).$$

Now the question is whether $x^2 + x + 2$ can be factored. We are looking for two numbers that add to 1 and multiply to 2. I can't think of a pair of numbers that do that. $24(x^2 + x + 2)$ is the final answer.

953. Simplify $\dfrac{x(x + 3) - 5(x + 3)}{4x^2 - 13x - 35}$

The numerator looks like a grouping problem that has been half completed. Factor an $x + 3$ out and we get $(x + 3)(x - 5)$.

The denominator is a general trinomial. We need to find two things that multiply to $-140x^2$ (the product of $4x^2$ and -35) and which add to $-13x$. These are larger numbers, and it may take a minute to find that $+7x$ and $-20x$ will do the job.

$$4x^2 - 13x - 35$$
$$= 4x^2 + 7x - 20x - 35$$
$$= x(4x + 7) - 5(4x + 7)$$
$$= (4x + 7)(x - 5)$$

The original fraction factors into $\dfrac{(x + 3)(x - 5)}{(4x + 7)(x - 5)} = \dfrac{x + 3}{4x + 7}$

The Complete Solutions and Answers

957. Joe likes to play baseball with himself. Standing in the middle of a field, he threw the ball east at 16 ft/sec. After waiting 3 seconds, he started running west at 5 ft/sec. How long did he run before he and the ball were 174 feet apart?

❶ Using the Let t = approach:

Let t = the number of seconds that Joe ran.

Then $t + 3$ = the number of seconds that the ball was heading east.

Then $5t$ = the number of feet that Joe ran. (He ran at 5 ft/sec for t seconds.)

Then $16(t + 3)$ = the number of feet the ball went. (It went at 16 ft/sec for t + 3 seconds.)

Finally, since the distance between the ball and Joe was 174 feet, we have the equation

$$5t + 16(t + 3) = 174$$

Using the distributive law $\quad 5t + 16t + 48 = 174$

Adding $\quad\quad\quad\quad\quad\quad 21t + 48 = 174$

Subtracting 48 from both sides $\quad\quad 21t = 126$

Dividing both sides by 21 $\quad\quad\quad t = 6$

Joe ran for 6 seconds.

❷ Using the Six Pretty Boxes approach:

	d	r	t
Joe			t
the ball			

→

	d	r	t
Joe			t
the ball			t + 3

↙

	d	r	t
Joe		5	t
the ball		16	t + 3

→

	d	r	t
Joe	5t	5	t
the ball	16(t+3)	16	t + 3

959. $-3 - (-12) = -3 + (+12) = 9$ (or +9) Subtracting a negative number is equivalent to adding a positive number.

960. ≤ means "less than or equal to."

977. $100 + (-5) = 95$ This is like a gain of 100 and a loss of five. The result is the same as a gain of 95.

The Complete Solutions and Answers

979. Darlene drove at 60 mph from her apartment to the Giant Bridal Mall. With her car loaded down with bridal stuff, she drove at 20 mph from the Giant Bridal Mall back to her apartment. It took 2 more hours to drive back to her apartment than it did to drive to the mall. How long did it take her to drive to the mall?

❶ Using the Let t = approach:

Let t = the number of hours it took Darlene to drive to the mall.

Then t + 2 = the number of hours to drive back to her apartment.

Then 60t = the number of miles to the mall.

Then 20(t + 2) = the number of miles back to her apartment.

Finally, since the distance to the mall is the same as the distance

from the mall, $$60t = 20(t + 2)$$

Using the distributive law $$60t = 20t + 40$$

Subtracting 20t from both sides $$40t = 40$$

Dividing both sides by 40 $$t = 1$$

It took Darlene one hour to drive from her apartment to the mall.

❷ Using the Six Pretty Boxes approach:

	distance	rate	time
to the mall			t
to her apt.			

→

	distance	rate	time
to the mall			t
to her apt.			t + 2

	distance	rate	time
to the mall		60	t
to her apt.		20	t + 2

→

	distance	rate	time
to the mall	60t	60	t
to her apt.	20(t + 2)	20	t + 2

980. Before the storm, my house was worth a million dollars. After the storm it was worth $100,000. The change from $1,000,000 to $100,000 is the same as $100,000 − $1,000,000 which equals −$900,000.

986. $-17 + (+7) = -10$ This is like a loss of 17 followed by a gain of seven. The result is the same as a loss of 10.

989. $-70 - (-30) = -70 + (+30) = -40$ Subtracting a negative number is equivalent to adding a positive number. A loss of 70 and a gain of 30 result in a net loss of 40.

990. Factor $x^2 - 2x - 24$

We are looking for two numbers that multiply to -24 and add to -2.

$$x^2 - 2x - 24 = (x - 6)(x + 4)$$

992.

$$6x - 5 \overline{) \begin{array}{l} 2x^2 + 3x + 6 + \frac{2}{6x - 5} \\ \hline 12x^3 + 8x^2 + 21x - 28 \end{array}}$$

$$\begin{array}{r}
12x^3 - 10x^2 \\
\hline
18x^2 + 21x \\
18x^2 - 15x \\
\hline
36x - 28 \\
36x - 30 \\
\hline
2
\end{array}$$

993.   ✏ was assigned to beta.

✂ was assigned to beta.

✱ was assigned to gamma.

All we need to check is whether each element in the domain was assigned to exactly one element (in the codomain). ✏ was assigned to exactly one element. ✂ was assigned to one element. (It happened to be the same element that ✏ was assigned to, but that is irrelevant.) ✱ was assigned to one element.

It's a function.

994. In order to find the slope of the line $4x + y = 12$, we first have to put the equation in the $y = mx + b$ form.

$$4x + y = 12$$
$$y = -4x + 12 \qquad \text{Subtracting } 4x \text{ from both sides.}$$

The slope is equal to -4.

997. Graph $x = 7$

If $x = 7$, then y could be any number.
So $(7, -3)$, $(7, 0)$, $(7, 1)$, $(7, 4)$, $(7, 9)$ are all on the graph.

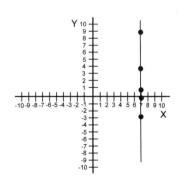

The Complete Solutions and Answers

999. When you graph x + y = 50, you are going to get some bigger numbers.

     If x = 0, then y = 50. We plot the point (0, 50).

     If y = 0, then x = 50. We plot the point (50, 0).

     If x = 20, then y = 30. We plot the point (20, 30).

     I need to change the numbering on the axes, so that the graph isn't two feet wide!

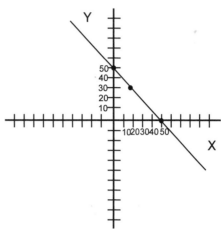

1001. −56/−7 = +8 If you multiply or divide two numbers with the same sign, the answer is positive.

1003. Factor $z^2 + 15z + 50$. We are looking for two numbers that add to 15 and multiply to 50. What numbers multiply to 50? 2 and 25, but they don't add to 15. 1 and 50, but they don't add to 15. 5 and 10 will work. $(z + 5)(z + 10)$.

1007.

Multiply top and bottom by $\sqrt{x + 3y}$

$$\frac{31y}{\sqrt{x + 3y}}$$

$$= \frac{31y\sqrt{x + 3y}}{\sqrt{x + 3y}\,\sqrt{x + 3y}}$$

$$= \frac{31y\sqrt{x + 3y}}{x + 3y}$$

1009. Solve $5x^2 + 9x = -3$

First, we place it in the general form $ax^2 + bx + c = 0$

$5x^2 + 9x = -3$ becomes $5x^2 + 9x + 3 = 0$ a = 5, b = 9, c = 3

We recite the quadratic formula minus b, plus or minus the square root of b squared minus four a c, all over two a, and simply write out the final answer:

$$x = \frac{-9 \pm \sqrt{81 - 4(5)(3)}}{10} = \frac{-9 \pm \sqrt{21}}{10}$$

The Complete Solutions and Answers

1010. Solve $10x^2 + 10x - 30 = 0$

I like to make my work as easy as possible. That's one reason I chose to become a mathematician. People who are history majors have to read a zillion books and write long term papers. People who are music majors have to practice five hours a day. (Really!) People who are psychology majors will have a tougher time finding a job.

For math majors, there is little that you have to memorize. You already did the memorizing when you learned the addition and multiplication tables. When I taught math in college, all the tests I gave were open book and open notes. What I wanted my students to spend their time on was learning how to do things like quadratic equations. I didn't want them to waste their time memorizing that the anti-derivative of $\frac{1}{u^2 + 1}$ was equal to arctan $u + C$. Stuff that they used frequently would memorize itself without much effort. Stuff that they didn't use frequently wasn't worth memorizing!

There are, sad to say, lazy teachers of math, of history, of chemistry. It is so much easier to have students memorize and memorize. The tests are much easier to write. What the students never learn to do is think. They just become efficient tape recorders. And after the semester is over, most of the stuff they crammed into their heads for the tests is soon forgotten.

So, it's my job to teach you more than 𝕄𝔼𝕮ℍ𝔸ℕ𝕀𝕮𝔸𝕃 ℙℝ𝕆𝕮𝔼𝔻𝕌ℝ𝔼𝕊. We are trying to solve $10x^2 + 10x - 30 = 0$.

How can we make our work simpler?

Divide through by 10 and get $x^2 + x - 3 = 0$.

Then use the quadratic formula:
$$x = \frac{-1 \pm \sqrt{1 - 4(1)(-3)}}{2}$$
$$x = \frac{-1 \pm \sqrt{13}}{2}$$

1017. Factor $30x^2 - 55x - 50$

First look for a common factor. $30x^2 - 55x - 50 = 5(6x^2 - 11x - 10)$
$6x^2 - 11x - 10$ is one of the harder trinomials. We look for two numbers that multiply to $-60x^2$ and add to $-11x$. That would be $4x$ and $-15x$. We break $6x^2 - 11x - 10$ into $6x^2 + 4x - 15x - 10$ and factor by grouping.
$2x(3x + 2) - 5(3x + 2) = (3x + 2)(2x - 5)$.
The final answer is $5(3x + 2)(2x - 5)$.

The Complete Solutions and Answers

1020. In a picture:

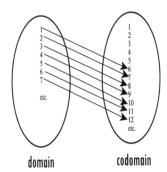

domain   codomain

Suppose the rule is: Assign to each element of the domain the number that is five larger than it. In symbols, assign to n, the number n + 5.

The range of this function is the set {6, 7, 8, 9, 10, 11, 12, . . .}.

1022. In order to find the slope of the line 3x + 7 = 2y we first have to put the equation in the y = mx + b form.

$$3x + 7 = 2y$$

Interchange the two sides. $$2y = 3x + 7$$

This is called the symmetric law of equality.

If A = B, then B = A.

Divide both sides by 2. $$y = (3/2)x + 7/2$$

It is now in the y = mx + b form. The slope is equal to 3/2.

1024. In a right triangle, the hypotenuse is equal to 20, and one leg is equal to 10. What is the length of the other leg? Simplify your answer (but do not approximate it).

By the Pythagorean theorem: $$10^2 + x^2 = 20^2$$
$$100 + x^2 = 400$$

| We ignore |
| $x = -\sqrt{300}$ |
| since we are dealing |
| with lengths. |

$$x^2 = 300$$
$$x = \sqrt{300}$$
$$x = \sqrt{100}\sqrt{3}$$
$$x = 10\sqrt{3}$$

1030. Not every element in the domain would be assigned an image in the codomain. For example, the number 3 would be assigned –1, which is not an element of the codomain.

1040. $\sqrt{45} + \sqrt{20} + \sqrt{5} = \sqrt{9}\sqrt{5} + \sqrt{4}\sqrt{5} + \sqrt{5}$
$$= 3\sqrt{5} + 2\sqrt{5} + \sqrt{5} = 6\sqrt{5}$$

The Complete Solutions and Answers

1044. Solve $3x^2 + 4x + 5 = 0$

It is in the general form: $ax^2 + bx + c = 0$

We recite the formula minus b, plus or minus the square root of b squared minus four a c, all over two a as we write the answer:

$$x = \frac{-4 \pm \sqrt{16 - 4(3)(5)}}{6}$$

$$x = \frac{-4 \pm \sqrt{-44}}{6}$$

Wait! We have the square root of a negative number.

You can't take the square root of a negative number.

There is no solution to $3x^2 + 4x + 5 = 0$.

1047. ✂ is assigned to both beta and gamma.

The definition of function is that each element in the domain is assigned to *exactly one* element in the codomain.

It is not a function.

1049. In order to find the slope of the line $5x - y = 45$ we first need to put the equation in the $y = mx + b$ form.

$$5x - y = 45$$

Transpose the 5x $-y = -5x + 45$

Multiply by -1 $y = 5x - 45$

The slope is equal to 5.

1050. Graph $x \geq 0$. In other words, graph all the points in which the x coordinate is greater than or equal to zero. For example, (3, 4), (3, 972), (3, − 393955), (0, 440), (9, 3999), (37972943, − 2), or (0, 0).

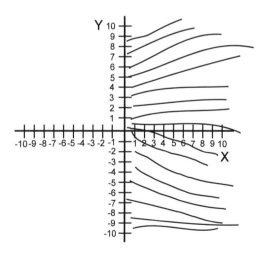

The Complete Solutions and Answers

1060. $\dfrac{4}{x-9} + \dfrac{2}{x-3}$

The smallest thing that both denominators can evenly divide into is called **the least common multiple**. In this case, the least common multiple of $x-9$ and $x-3$ is $(x-9)(x-3)$.

To do Interior Decoration we take each fraction and multiply top and bottom by something that will turn the denominator into the least common multiple.

$$\dfrac{4}{x-9} + \dfrac{2}{x-3} = \dfrac{4(x-3)}{(x-9)(x-3)} + \dfrac{2(x-9)}{(x-3)(x-9)}$$

$$= \dfrac{4(x-3) + 2(x-9)}{(x-9)(x-3)}$$

$$= \dfrac{4x-12+2x-18}{(x-9)(x-3)}$$

$$= \dfrac{6x-30}{(x-9)(x-3)}$$

$$= \dfrac{6(x-5)}{(x-9)(x-3)}$$

Since there are no common factors in the numerator and denominator, the fraction can not be simplified. (There is no need to multiply out your final answer unless you like doing extra work.)

1069. $\dfrac{2}{\sqrt{w}+5}$

When there is a binomial in the denominator, we multiply by the **conjugate**. The conjugate of $\sqrt{a}+7$ is $\sqrt{a}-7$.

The conjugate of $67+\sqrt{y}$ is $67-\sqrt{y}$.

The conjugate of $\sqrt{45a}-\sqrt{8xy}$ is $\sqrt{45a}+\sqrt{8xy}$.

The conjugate of $d-\sqrt{345678x}$ is $d+\sqrt{345678x}$.

For $\dfrac{2}{\sqrt{w}+5}$ we multiply top and bottom by $\sqrt{w}-5$.

$$\dfrac{2}{\sqrt{w}+5} = \dfrac{2(\sqrt{w}-5)}{(\sqrt{w}+5)(\sqrt{w}-5)} = \dfrac{2(\sqrt{w}-5)}{w-25}$$

Recall that $(x+y)(x-y) = x^2-y^2$.
That is why $(\sqrt{w}+5)(\sqrt{w}-5)$ equals $w-25$.

The Complete Solutions and Answers

1099. Factor $x^2 - 2x - 15$. Two numbers that multiply to -15 means that one of them is positive and the other is negative.

-3 and $+5$ don't work since they add to $+2$.

$+3$ and -5 will work. $(x + 3)(x - 5)$

1100. Joe and Darlene had a running contest. They each ran for 20 seconds. Darlene can run 3 ft/sec faster than Joe. Together they ran a total of 260 feet. How fast did Joe run? (No credit will be given unless you begin with Let r = . . . or use Six Pretty boxes.)

Let r = Joe's speed. (That's what we're trying to find.)

Then $r + 3$ = Darlene's speed.

Then $20r$ = how far Joe ran. (He ran 20 seconds at r ft/sec.)

Then $20(r + 3)$ = how far Darlene ran. (20 seconds at r + 3 ft/sec)

Then how far Joe ran plus how far Darlene ran equals 260 feet.

$$20r + 20(r + 3) = 260$$
$$20r + 20r + 60 = 260$$
$$40r + 60 = 260$$
$$40r = 200$$
$$r = 5 \quad \text{Joe ran 5 ft/sec.}$$

Using Six Pretty boxes:

	distance	rate	time
Joe	20r	r	20
Darlene	20(r + 3)	r + 3	20

1111. If we multiply 1,000,001 negative numbers together, the first 500,000 pairs of numbers will give a positive answer. That positive answer times the 1,000,001st negative number will give a final answer that is negative. ⋁⋁⋁⋁⋁⋁   ⋁⋁⋁⋁⋁⋁

+ + + + + +   ...   + + + + + + −

1122. ✏ was assigned to gamma. So far, so good.

✂ was assigned to alpha. So far, so good.

✳ wasn't assigned to anything. It's not a function.

Each element in the domain must be assigned.

1125. By the symmetric law of equality, $\pi = \dfrac{C}{d}$ becomes $\dfrac{C}{d} = \pi$.

The Complete Solutions and Answers

1130. To celebrate National Seafood Month, Joe went down to the wholesale market and bought a truck load of fish.

He could clean all of those fish in 30 days. Darlene could clean them all in 20 days. How long would it take them to clean that truck load of fish if they worked together?

Let x = the number of days for them to clean the fish if they worked together.

Then $\frac{1}{x}$ = the fraction of the fish they could clean in one day.

Since Joe, working alone, can clean them all in 30 days, he can clean $\frac{1}{30}$ of them in one day.

Since Darlene could clean them all in 20 days, she can clean $\frac{1}{20}$ of them in one day.

$$\frac{1}{30} + \frac{1}{20} = \frac{1}{x}$$

The least common denominator is 60x. (600x is not the *least* common denominator. It will work, but the arithmetic is harder.)

We multiply each term by 60x and cancel. The fractions disappear.

$$2x + 3x = 60$$
$$5x = 60$$
$$x = 12 \text{ days if they both work together.}$$

1136. Graph y ≥ 0. In other words, graph all the points in which the y coordinate is greater than or equal to zero.

For example, (33, 100), (−5, 8733), (−110, 30), (0, 0), (−3, π), (5, √3), (9, 9), or (979233.9832, 1).

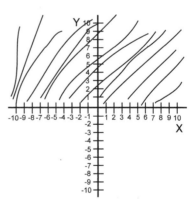

1140. Is it possible for a function to have a finite domain (translation: a set with a finite number of elements in it) and an infinite codomain (translation: a set with an infinite number of elements in it)?

No problem. Suppose the domain was {A, B} and the codomain was ℕ = {1, 2, 3, 4, 5, 6, . . .}.

One possible function would be A → 983 and B → 7000000.

The Complete Solutions and Answers

1200. Factor $y^2 - 6y - 16$. We want two numbers that multiply to -16 and add to -6. One of them must be positive and the other must be negative.
$+4$ and -4 don't work. They add to zero.
-16 and $+1$ don't work. They add to -15.
-2 and $+8$ don't work. They add to $+6$.
$+2$ and -8 will work. $(y + 2)(y - 8)$ is the final answer.

1203. Solve $\dfrac{3}{x - 1} + \dfrac{1}{2} = x - 1$

Make them all into fractions. $\dfrac{3}{x - 1} + \dfrac{1}{2} = \dfrac{x - 1}{1}$

To solve fractional equations we multiply through (like Santa delivering gifts) by the least common denominator, which is $2(x - 1)$

$$\frac{3(2)(x - 1)}{x - 1} + \frac{1(2)(x - 1)}{2} = \frac{(x - 1)(2)(x - 1)}{1}$$

All the denominators disappear.

$$3(2) + x - 1 = (2x - 2)(x - 1)$$
$$6 + x - 1 = 2x^2 - 4x + 2$$

Let's see if it will solve by factoring. Put everything on one side of the equation. $\qquad 0 = 2x^2 - 5x - 3$

Factoring $\qquad\qquad\qquad 0 = (2x + 1)(x - 3)$

Set each factor equal to zero $\quad 2x + 1 = 0 \quad$ OR $\quad x - 3 = 0$

Solve $\qquad\qquad\qquad\qquad x = -\dfrac{1}{2}$ OR $x = 3$

We must check each answer in the original equation. That is mandatory.
------------for $x = -\dfrac{1}{2}$

the original equation becomes $\quad \dfrac{3}{-3/2} + \dfrac{1}{2} \overset{?}{=} -\dfrac{1}{2} - 1$

$$-2 + \frac{1}{2} \overset{?}{=} -1\frac{1}{2} \qquad \text{true}$$

------------for $x = 3$

the original equation becomes $\quad \dfrac{3}{2} + \dfrac{1}{2} \overset{?}{=} 3 - 1 \qquad\qquad$ true

Both answers check. The complete solution is $x = -\dfrac{1}{2}$ or $x = 3$.

1204. How many different functions could have a domain equal to N and a codomain equal to $\{\bigstar\}$? N is the set of natural numbers $\{1, 2, 3, 4, 5, 6, 7, 8 \ldots\}$.

There is only one function possible. It would be the rule which assigns to each natural number $\bigstar$. So, for example, $3424 \rightarrow \bigstar$ and $98 \rightarrow \bigstar$.

The Complete Solutions and Answers

1205. The harder way to find where the line $y = 32x + 55$ intercepts (hits) the y-axis is to set x equal to zero and solve. That will give $y = 55$. Since the equation is in the $y = mx + b$ form (called the slope-intercept form), we can instantly state that the line hits the y-axis at $y = 55$ (since $b = 55$).

The question asks for *the point*. The point will be (0, 55).

1208.
$$4x^2 + 10 = 19$$
$$4x^2 = 9$$
$$x^2 = \frac{9}{4}$$
$$x = \pm\frac{3}{2} \text{ or } \pm 1.5$$

1212. $\dfrac{\sqrt{x} + 4}{\sqrt{x}}$

Multiply top and bottom by $\sqrt{x}$

$$\frac{(\sqrt{x} + 4)(\sqrt{x})}{(\sqrt{x})(\sqrt{x})} = \frac{(\sqrt{x} + 4)\sqrt{x}}{x}$$

OR $\dfrac{x + 4\sqrt{x}}{x}$ Either way is fine.

1220. $\dfrac{a}{\sqrt{a} + b}$

Multiply top and bottom by the conjugate of $\sqrt{a} + b$

$$\frac{a(\sqrt{a} - b)}{(\sqrt{a} + b)(\sqrt{a} - b)} = \frac{a(\sqrt{a} - b)}{a - b^2}$$

OR $\dfrac{a\sqrt{a} - ab}{a - b^2}$ Either way is fine.

1222. The mode average of 33, 34, 34, 35, 77, 77, 77, 298 is 77, because it is the most common number in the list.

1225. Simplify $\dfrac{x^7 + x^{-2}}{x^{-3}}$

Multiply top and bottom by x^3 $\dfrac{(x^7 + x^{-2})x^3}{x^{-3}\,x^3} = \dfrac{x^{10} + x}{1} = x^{10} + x$

The Complete Solutions and Answers

1241. Kingie uses 3 gallons of oil paint per hour when he's doing landscape paintings. Two gallons per hour when doing portraits. He only has 18 gallons of oil paint. Graph his possibilities. (Let x equal the number of hours he does landscapes and y, the number of hours he does portraits.)

If Kingie uses 3 gallons of oil paint per hour for landscapes and he paints for x hours, he will use 3x gallons. Similarly, he will use 2y gallons of paint for portraits.

$3x + 2y \leq 18$ is what we would like to graph.

We note that $x \geq 0$ and $y \geq 0$ since Kingie can't use a negative amount of paint. In the language of graphing, we will be working only in the first quadrant.

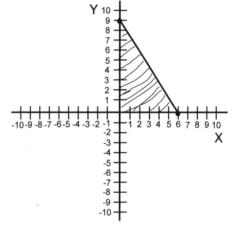

We will graph $3x + 2y = 18$ by point plotting.

We will use a solid line (and not a dashed line) because the original problem was $\leq$ (and not $<$).

If $x = 0$, the $y = 9$. The point $(0, 9)$.
If $y = 0$, then $x = 6$. The point $(6, 0)$.

The point $(0, 0)$ makes $3x + 2y \leq 18$ true. We shade the left side.

The point $(800, 873)$ makes $3x + 2y \leq 18$ false. We don't shade the right side.

1244. To simplify $\dfrac{x^9 - y^{-9}}{y^{-10}}$ we multiply top and bottom by y^{10}.

$$\frac{(x^9 - y^{-9})y^{10}}{y^{-10}\, y^{10}} = \frac{x^9 y^{10} - y}{y^0} = x^9 y^{10} - y \quad \text{since } y^0 = 1.$$

The Complete Solutions and Answers

1250. KITTENS University gave Fred 60¢ to spend for school supplies. Pencils cost 2¢ each. Pens cost 3¢ each. Let x equal the number of pencils he bought. Let y equal the number of pens he bought. Graph Fred's possibilities.

If Fred bought x pencils at 2¢ each, he paid 2x¢ for the pencils. Similarly, he paid 3y¢ for the pens.

His total purchase was $2x + 3y$. We are told that he could spend 60¢ at most. Therefore, $2x + 3y \leq 60$.

We first graph $2x + 3y = 60$. The easiest way might be just to find a couple of points on the line. If $x = 0$, then $y = 20$. The point (0, 20). If $y = 0$, then $x = 30$. The point (30, 0).

Since we have $\leq$ (and not just $<$) we graph a solid line (and not a dashed line).

Next, we test to see which side of the line we shade in.

Testing (0, 0) in $2x + 3y \leq 60$. True.

Testing (100, 100) in $2x + 3y \leq 60$. False.

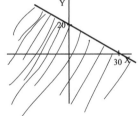

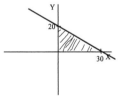

Now we need to make some slight adjustments in order to conform to reality.

Adjustment #1: Fred can't buy a negative number of pencils. So $x \geq 0$. That eliminates the shading to the left of the y-axis.

Adjustment #2: Fred can't buy a negative number of pens. So $y \geq 0$. That eliminates the shading below the x-axis.

Adjustment #3: Fred can't buy a fraction of a pencil or pen. So instead of filling in the whole triangle with shading, we should just graph what are called the **lattice points**.

(This problem is much harder than you might find in any other beginning algebra book. ☺ It's much closer to real life.)

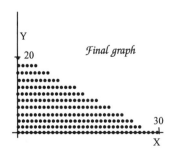

Final graph

The Complete Solutions and Answers

1252. Solve $x^2 + 3x - 6 = 5x$

Transpose the 5x to put it into the general form: $\qquad x^2 - 2x - 6 = 0$

Use the quadratic formula: $\qquad x = \dfrac{2 \pm \sqrt{4 - 4(1)(-6)}}{2}$

$x = \dfrac{2 \pm \sqrt{28}}{2} = \dfrac{2 \pm \sqrt{4}\sqrt{7}}{2} = \dfrac{2 \pm 2\sqrt{7}}{2} = \dfrac{2(1 \pm \sqrt{7})}{2} = 1 \pm \sqrt{7}$

1255. How many different functions could have a domain equal to {★} and a codomain equal to N? N is the set of natural numbers {1, 2, 3, 4, 5, 6, 7, 8 . . .}.

There are an infinite number of possible functions.

One example: Assign ★ to 3929396.

Second example: Assign ★ to 9879796606003.

Third example: Assign ★ to 1.

Each of these is a function since it assigns to each element in the domain exactly one element in the codomain.

1258. Consider the line that passes through (3, 7) and (8, 9).

   A) What is the change in y? (the rise) From 7 to 9 is a change of +2.

   B) What is the change is x? (the run) From 3 to 8 is a change of +5.

   C) What is the slope of this line? The slope (rise/run) in this case is $\dfrac{2}{5}$

1260. What is the point at which the line $y = 3.5x - 17$ hits the y-axis? Since it is in the $y = mx + b$ (slope-intercept form) we can instantly state that it hits at $y = -17$. The point is (0, -17).

1263. Is this a function?
The domain is {3, 5} and the codomain is {L, M, N} and the rule is the image of 3 is L and the image of 5 is L.

Does 3 have exactly one image? Yes.

Does 5 have exactly one image? Yes.

That's all we have to be concerned about. It is a function.

1265. $\quad 9x - 44 = 2x + 44$

$\qquad 7x - 44 = 44 \qquad\qquad$ Subtracting 2x from both sides.

$\qquad\quad 7x = 88 \qquad\qquad$ Adding 44 to both sides.

$\qquad\quad x = 88/7 \text{ or } 12\dfrac{4}{7}$

The Complete Solutions and Answers

1277. 2^5 is equal to $2 \times 2 \times 2 \times 2 \times 2 = 32$. (In the 𝔐ixed 𝔅ag section we sometimes take material from previous chapters or previous books.)

1280. Factor $x^2 + 20x + 36$. This is tough. There are a zillion pairs of numbers that multiply to 36.

1 and 36 add to 37.

4 and 9 add to 13.

6 and 6 add to 12.

2 and 18 add to 20. Bingo! We found them. $(x + 2)(x + 18)$.

     Note: Sometimes, there is no pair of numbers that work. Not every easy trinomial factors.

1313. $-22 - 7 = -22 - (+7) = -22 + (-7) = -29$ The subtraction of a positive number is the same as the addition of its negative.

$x - (+y)$ is the same as $x + (-y)$.

1316. $1!!!!! = 1!!!! = 1!!! = 1!! = 1! = 1$

1362. Complete this sentence: $w \geq y$ iff $y \leq w$.

1371. If you multiply together an even number of negative numbers, the answer will always be positive.

     If you multiply together an odd number of negative numbers, the answer will always be negative.

1375. Evaluate 4!! You enter 4 on the calculator. You hit the ! key and it reads 24. So $4!! = 24!$. Hitting the key a second time gives you 6.2045×10^{23}.

     If you had a giant calculator you could do 5!!.

5!! would first become 120!. Hitting the button a second time would give you $6.689502913449127057588118054090 \times 10^{198}$.

     If you tried 8!!, you might melt most calculators.

$8!! = 3.434359492761005746029956979448 \times 10^{168,186}$

This is a "fairly large" number.

     The number of possible chess games that could ever be played is estimated to be around 10^{120}.

The Complete Solutions and Answers

1378. Solve $x^2 + 4x - 2 = 0$

It is in general form: $ax^2 + bx + c = 0$.

Using the quadratic formula: $x = \dfrac{-4 \pm \sqrt{16 - 4(1)(-2)}}{2}$

$$x = \dfrac{-4 \pm \sqrt{24}}{2} \qquad \text{(line 1)}$$

The $\sqrt{24}$ can be simplified. $\sqrt{24} = \sqrt{4}\sqrt{6} = 2\sqrt{6}$.

Putting $2\sqrt{6}$ into line 1: $\qquad x = \dfrac{-4 \pm 2\sqrt{6}}{2}$

To simplify a fraction you use the seven famous words: Factor top. Factor bottom. Cancel like factors.

$$x = \dfrac{-4 \pm 2\sqrt{6}}{2} = \dfrac{2(-2 \pm \sqrt{6})}{2} = -2 \pm \sqrt{6}$$

1380. Some student might say that π is a rational number because it can be written as $\dfrac{\pi}{1}$. The definition of a rational number is any number than can be expressed as an *integer* divided by a non-zero *integer*. π is not an integer.

1387. Factor $w^2 + 6w - 40$. Since -40 is negative, one will be positive and one will be negative: -4 and $+10$ add to $+6$ and multiply to -40.

$\qquad (w - 4)(w + 10)$

1390. Let's play Guess the Function. Try to guess the rule that defines this function:

Nevada → Neither   Washington → Pac   Iowa → Neither   South Carolina → At   Argentina → At
Ireland → At   Kansas → Neither   California → Pac   Montana → Neither   Italy → Neither

The rule is: If it touches the Pacific Ocean, map it to Pac. If it touches the Atlantic, map it to At. If it touches neither, map it to Neither.

1391. What is the point at which the line $y + x = 50$ hits the x-axis? (Read carefully: the x-axis.) It hits the x-axis when y is equal to zero. Setting y equal to zero, $y + x = 50$ becomes $x = 50$.

The point where the line intecepts the x-axis is $(50, 0)$.

114

The Complete Solutions and Answers

1409. If you multiply together four negative numbers, the answer will be positive. For example, if we start with (–1)(–2)(–4)(–7). The first step is to multiply the first two numbers together: (+2)(–4)(–7). Then we multiply the +2 times the –4 and get: (–8)(–7). Finally, +56.

1411. Let the domain and codomain be the set $\mathbb{N}$. ($\mathbb{N}$ is the set of natural numbers $\{1, 2, 3, 4, 5, \ldots\}$.)

Consider the function defined by the rule: Assign to each number n in the domain, the number n^2 in the codomain.

The range of this function would be the set $\{1, 4, 9, 16, 25, 36, 49, 64, 81, 100, \ldots\}$, which is known as the set of perfect squares.

1420. He can build a brick wall in 18 hours. Working with his son, they can build that wall in 12 hours. How long would it take his son to build the wall if he worked alone?

Let x = the number of hours it would take his son to build the wall.

Then $\frac{1}{x}$ = the part of the wall the son could build in one hour.

Since the father can build the wall in 18 hours, he can build $\frac{1}{18}$ of the wall in one hour.

Since they can build the wall in 12 hours working together, they can build $\frac{1}{12}$ of the wall in one hour.

$$\frac{1}{18} + \frac{1}{x} = \frac{1}{12}$$

The least common denominator is 36x. Each of the denominators will divide evenly into 36x.

We multiply each term of the equation by 36x to eliminate the denominators.

$$\frac{1(36x)}{18} + \frac{1(36x)}{x} = \frac{1(36x)}{12}$$

$$2x + 36 = 3x$$

$$36 = x \quad \text{The son can build the wall in 36 hours.}$$

The Complete Solutions and Answers

1520. Factor $x^2 - 15x - 100$. Two numbers that multiply to -100. One of them must be negative and the other positive.
-20 and $+5$ multiply to -100 and add to -15 $\qquad$ $(x - 20)(x + 5)$

1524. Solve $x^2 - 5x - 2 = 0$
One quick way to see if it will factor is to look at $b^2 - 4ac$. If that turns out to be a perfect square, then it will factor. (Perfect squares = 1, 4, 9, 16, 25, 36, etc.) $b^2 - 4ac$ is $25 - (4)(1)(-2)$ which is 33. We didn't lose any effort. We can use that 33 when we use the quadratic formula.

$$x = \frac{5 \pm \sqrt{33}}{2} \qquad \text{We're done!}$$

1527. A) Can the domain be any set? Yes. The domain can be the set of natural numbers ($\{1, 2, 3, 4, 5, \ldots\}$) or it can be {Montana, Fillmore}.

B) Can the codomain be any set? Almost any set—except the empty set.

C) If you specify the domain and the codomain, have you specified the function? No. A function is not the domain nor is it the codomain. A function is any rule that associates to each element in the domain exactly one element in the codomain.

For example, if the natural numbers was the domain and $\{\text{✈}, \text{✉}, \text{☺}\}$ was the codomain, one possible function would be to assign each even number to ☺ and each odd number to ✉.

1529. Graph $2x - 3y < 12$
Graph the line $2x - 3y = 12$.

If $x = 0$, then $y = -4$. The point $(0, -4)$.

If $y = 0$, then $x = 6$. The point $(6, 0)$.

Graph a dashed line since the original equation is $<$ (and not $\leq$) .

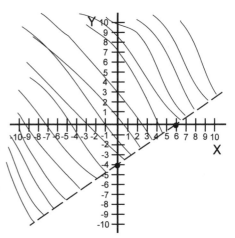

Testing $(0, 0)$, which is to the left of the line: $2(0) - 3(0) < 12$. Yes.
Testing $(10, 0)$, which is the right of the line: $2(10) - 3(0) < 12$. No.

The Complete Solutions and Answers

1583. $10^{-4} = \dfrac{1}{10,000} = 0.0001$

1585.   If I went on the number line from –7 to –5, by how much did my position change?

To go from –7 to –5 is the same as $-5 - (-7)$, which is equal to $-5 + (+7)$ which is a loss of 5 and a gain of 7, which is +2. The answer is positive because we are moving to the right on the number line.

1600. –400 < –4 is true. –400 is to the left of –4 on the number line. If you are 400 feet under the surface of the ocean, you are a lot deeper than if you are only 4 feet under the surface.

1602. How many times bigger is 8!! than the total number of possible chess games? Namely, how many times bigger is $10^{168,186}$ than 10^{120}?

If we want to know, for example, how many times bigger 100 is than 20, we divide: $\dfrac{100}{20}$ and say that 100 is 5 times larger than 20.

Since we want to find out how much bigger is $10^{168,186}$ than 10^{120} we

divide: $\dfrac{10^{168,186}}{10^{120}} = 10^{168,186 - 120} = 10^{168,066}$.

1613. $5w^3 = 5w^3$ is true by the reflexive law of equality.

1625. Suppose that you multiply together 81 integers. Suppose that 40 of them are positive, 40 are negative and one of them is zero. The 40 positive numbers will give you a positive answer. The 40 negative numbers will give you a positive answer. So these 80 numbers will give you a positive answer. Then when you multiply that times zero, you will get an answer of zero.

   In any product of numbers, if one of them is zero, the answer will be zero.

1630. $6 \cdot 8 + 60 / 10$
   = 48 + 6   multiplications and divisions (left to right)
   =   54   and then additions and subtractions.

The Complete Solutions and Answers

1633. If we are going to graph $2x + 3y = 4 + y$, let's first neaten up this equation by subtracting y from both sides. We get $2x + 2y = 4$.

Then we divide both sides by 2 and get $x + y = 2$. This equation is a lot easier to work with than $2x + 3y = 4 + y$.

If I let $x = 1$, then $x + y = 2$ becomes $1 + y = 2$, which gives a y value of 1. We plot the point (1, 1).

If I let $x = 5$, then $x + y = 2$ becomes $5 + y = 2$, which gives a y value of –3. We plot the point (5, –3).

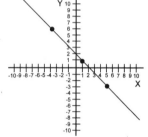

I'll get a third point since I tend to make silly arithmetic errors. If I let $x = -4$, then $x + y = 2$ becomes $-4 + y = 2$, which gives a y value of –6. We plot the point (–4, 6).

1635. Factor $16x^2 - 32$. It has been often said that you should look for a common factor first. There is a common factor of 16.

$16x^2 - 32 = 16(x^2 - 2)$

Since $x^2 - 2$ is not a difference of squares (2 is not a perfect square like 4 or 9 or 16 or 25 are), $16(x^2 - 2)$ is the final answer.

1663. No. It is not possible. It is never true that $x < x$.

1667. First you pick one of four hats, then you pick one of three watches. There are 4×3 ways to do that.

In general: *If there are x ways to do one thing and y ways to do another, there are xy ways of doing both.*

1680. Factor $x^2 - 25$. Both x^2 and 25 are perfect squares. x times x equals x^2. 5 times 5 equals 25.

It is a *difference* of squares.

The answer is $(x + 5)(x - 5)$.

1681. The reflexive law of equality states that any expression is equal to itself. For example, $x = x$ or $6 + 3w^2 = 6 + 3w^2$.

118

The Complete Solutions and Answers

1683. What number do you add to $x^2 - 18x$ to make it into a perfect square? Half of -18 is -9. Squaring -9, we get $+81$.

$x^2 - 18x + 81$ is a perfect square. It factors into $(x - 9)^2$. We can check that: $(x - 9)^2 = (x - 9)(x - 9) = x^2 - 9x - 9x + 81 = x^2 - 18x + 81$.

1685. Solve $\begin{cases} 2x - 5y = 4 \\ 6x + 5y = 32 \end{cases}$

Add the two equations $8x = 36$

Solve for x $x = 36/8 = 4\frac{1}{2}$

Back substitute into either of the two original equations.

(I choose the second equation.) $6(4\frac{1}{2}) + 5y = 32$

$$27 + 5y = 32$$
$$5y = 5$$
$$y = 1$$

The solution is $x = 4\frac{1}{2}$ and $y = 1$.

1690. $\frac{2}{3}$ as a ratio is 2:3.

1692. Fred worked for 3 hours hoeing weeds.
A professional worked 4 times as fast a Fred and worked for 8 hours. Together they hoed 210 rows. How fast did Fred work?

       Let r = the number of rows/hour that Fred could do.

       Then 4r = the number of rows/hour that the professional could do.

       Then 3r = the number of rows Fred did.

       Then 4r(8) = the number of rows that the professional did. (He worked at the rate of 4r for 8 hours.)

$$3r + 4r(8) = 210$$
$$3r + 32r = 210$$
$$35r = 210$$
$$r = 6 \text{ rows/hour was Fred's speed}$$

Using Six Pretty boxes:

	rows done	rate	time
Fred	3r	r	3
professional	4t(8)	4r	8

The Complete Solutions and Answers

1706. Forgiving your debt of $33 makes you $33 richer. Giving you $44 makes you $44 richer. Doing both makes you $77 richer.

1709. Joe got a toy parachute for his birthday. He threw it up in the air at the rate of 24 ft/sec. It floated down to his hand at the rate of 6 ft/sec. The whole round trip (up and down) took a total of 20 seconds. How many seconds was the parachute traveling upward?

❶ Using the Let t = . . . approach:

Let t = the number of seconds the parachute was traveling upward.

Then 20 – t = the number of seconds it was traveling downward.

(The total time was 20 seconds, so if it was going up for t seconds, it must have been going down to 20 – t seconds.)

Then 24t = the number of feet it went up. (It went up at the rate of 24 ft/sec for t seconds.)

Then 6(20 – t) = the number of feet it went down. (It went down at the rate of 6 ft/sec for 20 – t seconds.)

Finally, since the distance it traveled upward was the same as the distance it traveled downward, we have the equation $24t = 6(20 - t)$

distributive law	$24t = 120 - 6t$
add 6t to both sides	$30t = 120$
divide both sides by 30	$t = 4$

Joe's parachute went upward for 4 seconds.

❷ Using the Six Pretty Boxes approach:

	distance	rate	time
upward			t
downward			

→

	distance	rate	time
upward			t
downward			20 – t

↙

	distance	rate	time
upward		24	t
downward		6	20 – t

→

	distance	rate	time
upward	24t	24	t
downward	6(20 – t)	6	20 – t

1717. 444 ≥ 444 is true. Any number is ≥ to itself.

0.1 ≥ 0.01 is true. 0.1 is to the right of 0.01 on the number line.

–6 ≥ –98 is true. –6 is to the right of –98 on the number line.

$5\frac{1}{3}$ ≥ –100 is true. Any positive number is greater than or equal to any negative number.

The Complete Solutions and Answers

1719. The set $\{ x \mid x = 2n + 1$ where n is a natural number$\}$ is the same as the set $\{3, 5, 7, 9, 11, 13, \ldots\}$. To see that this is true, we first start with the natural numbers $\{1, 2, 3, 4, 5, \ldots\}$.

   If n = 1, then $2n + 1 = 3$.
   If n = 2, then $2n + 1 = 5$.
   If n = 3, then $2n + 1 = 7$. etc.

The smallest element of $\{3, 5, 7, 9, 11, 13, \ldots\}$ is 3.

1721. $y = x^2$ is not a linear equation. Plotting two points will not be enough to determine the shape of the curve. We need to plot enough points until we can figure out what the curve looks like. Then we draw the graph.

   If x = 0, then y = 0.   We plot (0, 0).
   If x = 1, then y = 1.   We plot (1, 1).
   If x = 2, then y = 4.   We plot (2, 4).
   If x = 3, then y = 9.   We plot (3, 9).
   If x = −1, then y = 1.   We plot (−1, 1).
   If x = −2, then y = 4.   We plot (−2, 4).
   If x = −3, then y = 9.   We plot (−3, 9).

The curve is starting to look like a U. (It's official name is a parabola. Pronounced per-RAB-a-leh.)

   We can now "connect the dots."

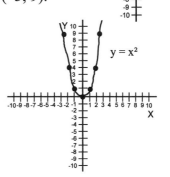

1725. Maple, blueberry, chocolate, oatmeal, strawberry, and cinnamon. There are six possible choices for the flavor on the bottom. Then five choices for the next layer. And four for the next. Etc. There are 6! possible arrangements. 6! = 720. Either 6! or 720 are acceptable answers.

1726. Factor $100x^2 - 49$.
10x times 10x equals $100x^2$.
7 times 7 equals 49.   The final answer is $(10x + 7)(10x - 7)$.

The Complete Solutions and Answers

1730. When Fred jogs for one minute, he burns 5 Calories. When he works out with weights, he burns 4 Calories each minute. He wishes to burn at least 20 Calories.

If he burns 5 Calories per minute while jogging, then he burns 5x Calories in x minutes.

If he burns 4 Calories per minute while working out with weights, then he burns 4y Calories in y minutes.

We want to graph $5x + 4y \geq 20$.

First we graph $5x + 4y = 20$. We will do that by point plotting. If x = 0, then y would equal 5. The point (0, 5) is on the line. If y = 0, then x would equal 4. The point (4, 0) is on the line.

(You could have chosen harder numbers. You could have let x equal 10. Then $5(10) + 4y = 20$ would have given y = $-7\frac{1}{2}$. I chose easy values for x and y to keep my work easy.)

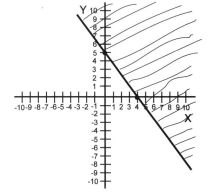

We test each side of the line. The point (0, 0) is on the left of the line. Putting (0, 0) into the original inequality gives: $5(0) + 4(0) \geq 20$. This is false. The point (100, 100) is on the right side of the line. Putting (100, 100) into the original inequality gives: $5(100) + 4(100) \geq 20$. This is true.

I shade in the right side of the line.

I need to make an adjustment. The number of minutes that Fred jogs can't be negative. Translation: $x \geq 0$.

The number of minutes he works out with weights can't be negative. Translation: $y \geq 0$.

The final graph will be:

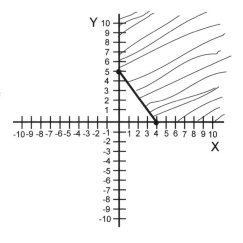

122

The Complete Solutions and Answers

1748. If we multiply eight negative numbers together, the answer will be positive. One way to look at it would be to notice that the first pair of negative numbers will be positive. The second and third pair of negative numbers will be positive. And the last pair will be positive.

$$(-)(-) \quad (-)(-) \quad (-)(-) \quad (-)(-)$$
$$\searrow\swarrow \quad \searrow\swarrow \quad \searrow\swarrow \quad \searrow\swarrow$$
$$(+) \qquad (+) \qquad (+) \qquad (+)$$

1750. Factor $7w^2 - 49$. This is not a difference of squares. $7w^2$ is not a perfect square.

Besides, as everyone knows, you always look for a common factor first. $7w^2 - 49 = 7(w^2 - 7)$. Since $w^2 - 7$ is not a difference of squares, the final answer is $7(w^2 - 7)$.

1753.
$$\cfrac{\dfrac{2x^2 - 7x - 30}{30x^2 - 30x - 600}}{\dfrac{x^2 - 36}{5x + 20}}$$

This complex fraction is one fraction, namely, $\dfrac{2x^2 - 7x - 30}{30x^2 - 30x - 600}$ divided by another fraction, namely, $\dfrac{x^2 - 36}{5x + 20}$

so we turn it into a division of fractions problem:

$$\frac{2x^2 - 7x - 30}{30x^2 - 30x - 600} \div \frac{x^2 - 36}{5x + 20}$$

Invert the fraction following the $\div$ sign $\quad \dfrac{2x^2 - 7x - 30}{30x^2 - 30x - 600} \times \dfrac{5x + 20}{x^2 - 36}$

Multiply $\quad = \dfrac{(2x^2 - 7x - 30)(5x + 20)}{(30x^2 - 30x - 600)(x^2 - 36)}$

Simplify $\quad = \dfrac{(2x + 5)(x - 6)5(x + 4)}{30(x + 4)(x - 5)(x + 6)(x - 6)}$ (factor top, factor bottom)

$$= \frac{(2x + 5)}{6(x - 5)(x + 6)} \quad \text{(cancel like factors)}$$

The Complete Solutions and Answers

1830. If you multiply together 40 different integers, and 21 of them are positive and the rest are negative, then we have a product of 21 positive numbers and 19 negative numbers.

    The 21 positive numbers gives a positive answer (+).

    The 19 negative numbers gives a negative answer (−).

    The product of the 21 positive (+) and the 19 negative (−) will be negative.

1832. To graph $y = x^3$, we need to plot enough points to determine the shape of the curve.

    If $x = 0$, then $y = 0$.   We plot $(0, 0)$. The curve passes through the origin.

    If $x = 1$, then $y = 1$.   We plot $(1, 1)$.

    If $x = 2$, then $y = 8$.   We plot $(2, 8)$.

    If $x = -1$, then $y = -1$. We plot $(-1, -1)$.

    If $x = -2$, then $y = -8$. We plot $(-2, -8)$.

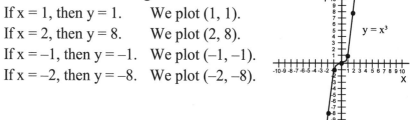

1834. $x^{-5} = \dfrac{1}{x^5}$

1835. $\dfrac{\dfrac{y^2 + 13y + 40}{y^2 - 7y - 44}}{\dfrac{2y^2 + 13y - 24}{2y^2 - 25y + 33}}$

One fraction divided by another we turn into a division of fractions

$$\frac{y^2 + 13y + 40}{y^2 - 7y - 44} \div \frac{2y^2 + 13y - 24}{2y^2 - 25y + 33}$$

Invert and multiply
$$= \frac{(y^2 + 13y + 40)(2y^2 - 25y + 33)}{(y^2 - 7y - 44)(2y^2 + 13y - 24)}$$

Factor top and factor bottom $= \dfrac{(y + 5)(y + 8)(2y - 3)(y - 11)}{(y - 11)(y + 4)(2y - 3)(y + 8)}$

Cancel like factors $= \dfrac{y + 5}{y + 4}$

The Complete Solutions and Answers

1836. What can you say about the sum (addition) of a positive number and a negative number? You can say . . . nothing!

Sometimes the answer is positive: $(+100) + (-3) = +97$.

Sometimes the answer is negative: $(+6) + (-27) = -21$.

Sometimes the answer is zero: $(+9873) + (-9873) = 0$.

1844. $36 / 9 \cdot 4$

$= 4 \cdot 4$ You do multiplication and division left to right.

$= 16$

1850. Darlene has weak dishwashing liquid that contains 17% soap. She also has strong dishwashing liquid that contains 37% soap.

Darlene just purchased a dishwashing robot. When she read the directions, she found out that the robot would only work if you gave it 444 ounces of dishwashing liquid that contained 22% soap.

How much of each dishwashing liquid should Darlene use?

❶ Using the Let x = . . . approach:

Let x = the number of ounces of weak dishwashing liquid used.

Then $444 - x$ = the number of ounces of strong used.

Then $0.17x$ = ounces of soap contributed by the weak.

Then $0.37(444 - x)$ = ounces of soap contributed by the strong dishwashing liquid.

Finally, since we want 97.68 (22% of 444) ounces of soap in the final mixture, we have the equation $0.17x + 0.37(444 - x) = 97.68$

distributive property	$0.17x + 164.28 - 0.37x = 97.68$
combine	$-0.2x + 164.28 = 97.68$
add 0.2x to both sides	$164.28 = 97.68 + 0.2x$
subtract 97.68 from both sides	$66.6 = 0.2x$
divide both sides by 0.2	$333 = x$

Darlene should use 333 ounces of the weak and 111 ounces of strong dishwashing liquid.

❷ Using the Six Pretty boxes approach:

	soap	percent	ounces used
weak liquid	$0.17x$	17%	x
strong liquid	$0.37(444 - x)$	37%	$444 - x$

The Complete Solutions and Answers

1889. $-5 + \underline{\ ?\ } = 15$ is the same as asking, "What do you add to -5 to get 15?" This is the same as asking, "What is the gain in going from -5 to 15?" That is $15 - (-5)$ which equals $15 + (+5) = 20$. (or $+20$)

1891. $\begin{cases} 7x + 3y = 43 \\ 4x - 3y = 1 \end{cases}$

$\qquad\qquad 11x = 44 \qquad$ Adding the two equations. The y-terms disappear.

$\qquad\qquad\ \ x = 4 \qquad$ Dividing both sides by 11.

To get the value of y, take $x = 4$ and put that value into any equation containing both variables.

Put $x = 4$ into the first equation $(7x + 3y = 43)$ and obtain:

$7(4) + 3y = 43$

$\ \ 28 + 3y = 43$

$\qquad\ 3y = 15$

$\qquad\ \ y = 5$

The final answer is $x = 4$ and $y = 5$.

1893. $\{\, y \mid y$ is an integer and $y < -4 \,\} \cup \{\, z \mid z$ is a natural number$\} = \{\ldots -6, -5, 1, 2, 3, 4, \ldots\}$

Or you could have written your answer as
$\{\, x \mid x$ is an integer and $x < -4$ or $x > 0 \,\}$.

Or you could have written: $\{\, z \mid z$ is an integer and $z \leq -5$ or $z \geq 1 \,\}$.

Or you could have written: $\{\, w \mid w$ is any integer except $-4, -3, -2, -1$ or $0 \,\}$.

1894. Solve by elimination $\begin{cases} 6x + 7y = 3 \\ -6x - 7y = 1 \end{cases}$

Adding the two equations we get $0 = 4$. (Both unknowns drop out.) The equations are inconsistent. There is no solution.

If there were a solution, say $x = 5$ and $y = 40$, that made both equations true, then $x = 5$ and $y = 40$ would have to make $0 = 4$ also true. But nothing will ever make $0 = 4$ true. Therefore, the original pair of equations has no solution.

If you had graphed these two equations, you would have gotten parallel lines.

The Complete Solutions and Answers

1898. Factor $4x^2 + 25$. This is not a *difference* of squares. It can not be factored.

1900. A pure quadratic equation is an equation that:

        i) contains an x^2 term,

        ii) doesn't contain an x term,

        iii) doesn't contain any x^3, x^4, x^5, etc. terms.

1903. Solve $12x + 7 = 6x^2$

Put x^2 and x terms on one side of the equation. $\quad 7 = 6x^2 - 12x$

Make the coefficient of the x^2 term equal
    to one by dividing through by six. $\qquad \dfrac{7}{6} = x^2 - 2x$

Complete the square. Half of -2 is -1, and
    -1 squared is $+1$. $\qquad \dfrac{7}{6} + 1 = x^2 - 2x + 1$

Arithmetic on the left side and
    factor the right side. $\qquad \dfrac{13}{6} = (x - 1)^2$

Take the square root of both sides and
    put a $\pm$ on the number. $\qquad \pm\sqrt{\dfrac{13}{6}} = x - 1$

Transpose the -1. $\qquad 1 \pm \sqrt{\dfrac{13}{6}} = x$

1904. Let $x = 0.77327732773277327732.\dots$ (line 1)

    Then $10000x = 7732.7732773277327732.\dots$ (line 2)

Subtracting line 1 from line 2: $\quad 9999x = 7732.0000000$

Divide both sides by 9999: $\qquad x = 7732/9999$

1906. You actually looked up this answer!
The answer is . . . C).

    Alternative A) would have made sense if it had been: Red, if one twirls yesterday's frog. That would have been the correct answer to the question, "What color would Darlene see if you took her pet frog that she owned yesterday and spun it around?"

The Complete Solutions and Answers

1919. Inside the army transport van, Fred counted the bugs in the van at the rate of 16/minute. After a while he switched to counting pieces of gum stuck to the wall of the van at the rate of 20/minute. It was easier to count the pieces of gum since they didn't move around.

After a total of 18 minutes of counting, he had counted the same number of bugs as pieces of gum. How long had he been counting the bugs?

For fun, ❷ let's start with the Six Pretty Boxes approach first:

	number	number per minute	minutes
bugs			t
gum			

→

	number	number per minute	minutes
bugs			t
gum			18 − t

	number	number per minute	minutes
bugs		16	t
gum		20	18 − t

→

	number	number per minute	minutes
bugs	16t	16	t
gum	20(18 − t)	20	18 − t

Finally, since the number of bugs he counted was equal to the number of pieces of gum he counted, we have the equation

$16t = 20(18 - t)$

$16t = 360 - 20t$ distributive property

$36t = 360$ add 20t to both sides

$t = 10$ divide both sides by 36

Fred spent 10 minutes counting bugs

❶ Using the Let t = . . . approach:

Let t = the number of minutes Fred counted bugs.

Then 18 − t = the number of minutes Fred counted pieces of gum.

(He spent t minutes counting bugs and 18 − t minutes counting pieces of gum so that the total adds to 18. t + 18 − t does equal 18.)

Then 16t = number of bugs counted.

Then 20(18 − t) = number of pieces of gum counted.

1921. $\notin$ means "is not an element of." For example, $\Re \notin \{A, \#, \mathbf{3}\}$.

1926. Fill in the blank: A proportion is the equality of two **ratios**.

For example: $\dfrac{1}{2} = \dfrac{3}{6}$ or $\dfrac{1 \text{ cup}}{1 \text{ quart}} = \dfrac{1 \text{ quart}}{1 \text{ gallon}}$

The Complete Solutions and Answers

1928. Haydn wrote the "Sun" quartets five times as long ago as Robert Frost wrote "In the Clearing."

Sixteen years from now, the "Sun" quartets will be four times as old as "In the Clearing." How old is "In the Clearing" today?

Let x = the current age of "In the Clearing."

Then 5x = the current age of the "Sun" quartets.

Then x + 16 = the age of "In the Clearing" 16 years from now.

Then 5x + 16 = the age of the "Sun" quartets 16 years from now.

Finally, since 16 years from now the age of the "Sun" quartets will be four times as old as "In the Clearing," we have the equation:

$$5x + 16 = 4(x + 16)$$
$$5x + 16 = 4x + 64$$
$$x + 16 = 64$$
$$x = 48$$

The current age of "In the Clearing" is 48 years.

1930. $z - 7 = 44w$ becomes
$$z = 44w + 7$$

1933. If a rectangle has an area of 56 square inches, and its length is 8 inches, what is the length of the perimeter?

The area of a rectangle is length × width. In this problem, 8w = 56. The width must be 7 inches.

8 inches

w | 56 square inches

The perimeter is the distance around the outside. In a rectangle it is two lengths plus two widths.

In this problem it would be 2(8) + 2(7) which is 30 inches.

1935. Graphing $3x - 3 = 9y$ if y = 0, then x = 1   plot (1, 0)

if y = 3, then x = 10   plot (10, 3)

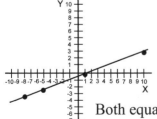

It's easier to name y-values and then find x-values in this case.

Graphing $x - 3y = 1$

if y = –2, then x = –5   plot (–5, –2)

if y = –3, then x = –8   plot (–8, –3)

Both equations plot the same line. They are dependent equations. Whatever makes one equation true will make the other one true.

The Complete Solutions and Answers

1936. $3962^1 = 3962$.

Anything to the first power is equal to itself: $x^1 = x$ for all x.

1939. $36y^2 - z^2 = (6y + z)(6y - z)$

Some people write their z's so that they look like 2s.

(English majors know that you use apostrophes in writing the plurals of letters but not numbers. Some non-English majors also know that.)

Some people cross their z's so they won't be mistaken for 2s. They write *z̸*.

1942. Solve $x^2 + 5x - 36 = 0$ by *factoring* and then solve it by *completing the square.*

To solve by factoring, place everything on one side. (That has already been done.)

Then factor. $\qquad (x - 4)(x + 9) = 0$

Review: You looked for two numbers that added to +5 and multiplied to −36. Those numbers are −4 and + 9. Then the factors are (x − 4)(x + 9).

The set each factor equal to zero. $\qquad x - 4 = 0 \ \ OR \ \ x + 9 = 0$

Then solve each equation. $\qquad x = 4 \ \ OR \ \ x = -9$

To solve by completing the square, first make sure that the coefficient of the x^2 term is equal to one. (It already is in this case.)

Then transpose the number to the right side and leave the x^2 and the x-term on the left. $\qquad x^2 + 5x = 36$

Then complete the square. $\qquad x^2 + 5x + \dfrac{25}{4} = 36 + \dfrac{25}{4}$

Review: You take half of 5. That is $\dfrac{5}{2}$. Then you square $\dfrac{5}{2}$ and get $\dfrac{25}{4}$ and you add that to both sides.

Factor the left. Add the right numbers. $\qquad (x + \dfrac{5}{2})^2 = \dfrac{169}{4}$

Review: Adding $36 + \dfrac{25}{4} = \dfrac{36}{1} + \dfrac{25}{4} = \dfrac{36(4)}{1(4)} + \dfrac{25}{4} = \dfrac{144 + 25}{4}$

Take the square root of both sides, adding $\pm$ to the right side. $\qquad x + \dfrac{5}{2} = \pm\dfrac{13}{2}$

Transpose the $\dfrac{5}{2}$ $\qquad x = \dfrac{-5}{2} \pm \dfrac{13}{2} = \dfrac{8}{2}$ or $\dfrac{-18}{2} = 4 \text{ or } -9$

The Complete Solutions and Answers

1945. Why did we teach completing the square?
A) We did it just to get the quadratic formula. It was just done to inflict pain on the reader.
B) There was a second reason mentioned in the textbook why we learned completion of the square.
C) There has gotta be another use for completing the square, but it wasn't mentioned in the text.

This is a psychology test! If you selected alternative A), that may indicate paranoia. (= someone is out to get you)

If you selected alternative B), that indicates delusional tendencies. You have seen stuff that isn't there.

Alternative C) is the mentally healthy answer.

And a healthy curiosity might elicit the obvious question: "What other use might completion of the square have?"

Answer: One example of a use will come in second semester calculus. As everyone (who has studied second semester calculus) knows, the anti-derivative of $\dfrac{1}{u^2 + 1}$ is arctan u + C.

Time Out!

In case you're dying to know what all that calculus stuff meant . . .

C is any constant. That's the easy part.

u is any expression containing x's.

arctan u is (hold onto your hat!) the acute angle A, such that if you draw a right triangle with angle A, then the side opposite to angle A divided by the side adjacent to A will equal u/1. (This is all explained in trigonometry.)

Given two sets (the domain and the codomain), a **function** is a rule which associates to each element of the domain exactly one element of the codomain. (Explained in Chapter 11 of *Life of Fred: Beginning Algebra Expanded Edition.*)

Given a curve where y is a function of x, the **derivative function** assigns to every value of x the slope of the tangent to the curve at x. (Slope is also explained in Chapter 11 of *Life of Fred: Beginning Algebra Expanded Edition.*) (continued on next page)

The Complete Solutions and Answers

> Inverse functions are explained in *Life of Fred: Advanced Algebra.*
> The **anti-derivative** is the inverse function of the derivative function.

Now that you know exactly (cough! cough!) what the anti-derivative of $\dfrac{1}{u^2 + 1}$ means, you just might understand why it wasn't mentioned in a beginning algebra book.

Now that we've gone this far, we might as well give an example of the use of completing the square.

Suppose I want to put $\dfrac{1}{x^2 + 6x + 14}$ into the form $\dfrac{1}{u^2 + 1}$ where u is some expression in x.

I complete the square. I know I want a 9, not a 14. I break the 14 into 9 + 5.

$$\frac{1}{x^2 + 6x + 14} \quad \text{becomes} \quad \frac{1}{x^2 + 6x + 9 + 5}$$

$$\text{which becomes} \quad \frac{1}{(x + 3)^2 + 5} \qquad \text{(line 1)}$$

and now if I let x + 3 equal u, we get $\dfrac{1}{u^2 + 5}$

Wait! I, your reader, object. You were supposed to get $\dfrac{1}{u^2 + 1}$ You have a $u^2 + 5$ in the denominator.

Oops! I should have let x + 3 equal $\sqrt{5}\,u$, not u.　　　(line 2)

Then line 1 would have become $\dfrac{1}{5u^2 + 5}$

and factoring out the 5, we would get $\qquad (\dfrac{1}{5})\,\dfrac{1}{u^2 + 1}$

whose anti-derivative is $(\dfrac{1}{5})$ arctan u

which is $\dfrac{1}{5}$ arctan $\dfrac{x + 3}{\sqrt{5}}$ 　　　　since u = $\dfrac{x + 3}{\sqrt{5}}$ from line 2.

This may have been a bit fast—covering a ton of concepts from parts of Beginning Algebra that you haven't had yet, material from Advanced Algebra, Trig, and Calculus. When we actually teach this material, we will go a lot more s-l-o-w-l-y. I promise.

The Complete Solutions and Answers

2000. Factor $x^6 - 100$.

x^3 times x^3 equals x^6.

This is a difference of squares. $(x^3 + 10)(x^3 - 10)$

2001. Joe likes to watch the circus on television. His three favorite acts are the goat, the dog and the elephant. For every 5 hours of watching goat acts, he watched 7 hours of dog acts and 8 hours of elephant acts.

All together, he watched 4,000 hours of these three types of acts. How many hours did he watch each of them?

5x   7x   8x

The acts are in the continued ratio of 5:7:8.

Or 5x:7x:8x.

$5x + 7x + 8x = 4000$

$20x = 4000$

$x = 200$

He watched the goat acts for 5x hours, which is 5(200) = 1,000 hours.

He watched the dog acts for 7x hours, which is 7(200) = 1,400 hours.

He watched the elephant acts for 8x hours, which is 8(200) = 1,600 hours.

2050. Factor $9x^{40} - y^8z^8$. $(3x^{20} + y^4z^4)(3x^{20} - y^4z^4)$

2051. $\dfrac{\dfrac{x^2 + 9x + 18}{2x^2 + 13x + 20}}{\dfrac{x^2 + 2x - 24}{x^2 - 16}}$

This is the easiest kind of complex fraction. It is one fraction divided by another. We write it as one fraction divided by another:

$= \dfrac{x^2 + 9x + 18}{2x^2 + 13x + 20} \div \dfrac{x^2 + 2x - 24}{x^2 - 16}$

$= \dfrac{x^2 + 9x + 18}{2x^2 + 13x + 20} \times \dfrac{x^2 - 16}{x^2 + 2x - 24}$ Invert and multiply.

$= \dfrac{(x^2 + 9x + 18)(x^2 - 16)}{(2x^2 + 13x + 20)(x^2 + 2x - 24)}$ Top times top. Bottom times bottom.

$= \dfrac{(x + 3)(x + 6)(x + 4)(x - 4)}{(2x + 5)(x + 4)(x + 6)(x - 4)}$ Factor top. Factor bottom.

$= \dfrac{x + 3}{2x + 5}$ Cancel like factors.

2056.
$$\dfrac{\dfrac{3}{x+2} - \dfrac{3x+1}{x^2+5x+6}}{\dfrac{7}{x+5} - \dfrac{7x+4}{x^2+7x+10}}$$

This is not just one fraction divided by another.

The hard way to do this would be to combine the top two fractions (by subtracting) and combine the bottom two fractions (again, by subtracting) and then you could have one fraction divided by another.

The easier way when you have a mess like this (where it isn't just one fraction divided by another fraction) is to ① first factor all the little denominators.

$$\dfrac{\dfrac{3}{x+2} - \dfrac{3x+1}{(x+2)(x+3)}}{\dfrac{7}{x+5} - \dfrac{7x+4}{(x+2)(x+5)}}$$

② Now find the least common multiple of all those little denominators. (Translation: Find the smallest thing that each of the baby denominators will divide evenly into.) In this case, it is $(x+2)(x+3)(x+5)$.

③ Now multiply the giant fraction by $\dfrac{(x+2)(x+3)(x+5)}{(x+2)(x+3)(x+5)}$

Translation: That's multiplying the giant fraction by 1, so it doesn't change the value of the fraction.

Second translation: Multiply the numerator of each *term* by $(x+2)(x+3)(x+5)$.

The giant fraction becomes
$$\dfrac{\dfrac{3(x+2)(x+3)(x+5)}{x+2} - \dfrac{(3x+1)(x+2)(x+3)(x+5)}{(x+2)(x+3)}}{\dfrac{7(x+2)(x+3)(x+5)}{x+5} - \dfrac{(7x+4)(x+2)(x+3)(x+5)}{(x+2)(x+5)}}$$

And—poof!—all the fractions-within-fractions stuff disappears by cancelling and you have $\dfrac{3(x+3)(x+5) - (3x+1)(x+5)}{7(x+2)(x+3) - (7x+4)(x+3)}$

Multiply out the top and the bottom and combine $\dfrac{8x+40}{10x+30}$ and

The Complete Solutions and Answers

factor $\dfrac{8(x+5)}{10(x+3)}$ which reduces to $\dfrac{4(x+5)}{5(x+3)}$

2060. Solve $x^2 = 64$.

  $x = \pm 8$. This could also be written as $x = 8$ or $x = -8$.

2066. $\dfrac{6}{3 - \sqrt{z}}$

Multiply by the conjugate of $3 - \sqrt{z}$ which is $3 + \sqrt{z}$

$$\dfrac{6(3 + \sqrt{z})}{(3 - \sqrt{z})(3 + \sqrt{z})} = \dfrac{6(3 + \sqrt{z})}{9 - z}$$

2072. Drawing in a rise over run triangle, we note that the rise is negative and the run is positive.

  Therefore, rise/run is negative.

  Therefore the slope is negative.

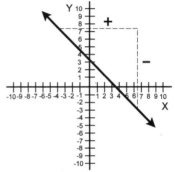

2100. Solve by elimination $\begin{cases} 8x + 12y = 20 \\ 2x + 3y = 5 \end{cases}$

Multiply the second equation by -4.

The pair of equations becomes $\begin{cases} 8x + 12y = 20 \\ -8x - 12y = -20 \end{cases}$

Add the two equations. We get $0 = 0$. Both variables drop out.

Since $0 = 0$ is always true, any ordered pair (a, b) that makes one equation true will make the other equation true.

  The equations are dependent.

  If you were to graph them, they would be the same line drawn twice.

2104. The whole numbers are $\{0, 1, 2, 3, 4 \ldots\}$. The natural numbers are $\{1, 2, 3, 4 \ldots\}$. The only number that is a whole number and not a natural number is zero.

The Complete Solutions and Answers

2108. Solve $\dfrac{7}{3x} - 6x = 5$

This is a fractional equation. We multiply through by 3x and that will clear away the denominator.

$$\dfrac{7(3x)}{3x} - 6x(3x) = 5(3x)$$

$$7 - 18x^2 = 15x$$

We will see if we can solve it by factoring. If that doesn't work, we resort to the quadratic formula.

Put everything on one side of the equation $0 = 18x^2 + 15x - 7$
One of the harder trinomials.
Look for expressions that multiply to $-126x^2$ $(18x)(-7)$
and that add to $15x$.

A trick . . . 126 is such a big number. We could factor it into 18 times 7 (because that's what we multiplied to get 126 in the first place). Then we could factor (18)(7) even further. (9)(2)(7) Even further into (3)(3)(2)(7). This is called the **prime factorization** of 126.

In later mathematics, we will prove that every natural number has exactly one prime factorization—assuming the order of the primes is not considered.

Then we will find mathematical worlds in which prime factorization is not unique.

Now, back to our job of juggling (3)(3)(2)(7) into two piles so that—oops! We want them to multiply to -126, not 126. So we want $(-1)(3)(3)(2)(7)$ to be in two piles so that they add to 15.

First try: $(-1)(3)(3)$ and $(2)(7)$ -9 and 14 add to 5 ☹
Second try: $(-1)(2)(3)$ and $(3)(7)$ -6 and 21 add to 15 ☺

So $-6x$ and $21x$ multiply to $-126x$ and add to $15x$.
We break $18x^2 + 15x - 7$ into $18x^2 - 6x + 21x - 7$ and factor by grouping.
$6x(3x - 1) + 7(3x - 1) = (3x - 1)(6x + 7)$
Set each factor equal to zero $3x - 1 = 0$ OR $6x + 7 = 0$
Solve $x = \dfrac{1}{3}$ OR $x = -\dfrac{7}{6}$
We must check each solution.

--------for $x = \dfrac{1}{3}$ the original equation becomes $\dfrac{7}{1} - 2 \overset{?}{=} 5$ true

--------for $x = -7/6$ the original equation becomes $\dfrac{7}{3(-7/6)} + 7 \overset{?}{=} 5$

The Complete Solutions and Answers

which is $\dfrac{7}{-7/2} + 7 \overset{?}{=} 5$ which is true.

The complete solution is $x = \dfrac{1}{3}$ or $x = -\dfrac{7}{6}$

2121. $\dfrac{\dfrac{x+2}{x+6} - \dfrac{x+8}{x^2+4x-12}}{\dfrac{x^2+11x-8}{x^2+9x-22} - \dfrac{x-1}{x-2}}$

① Factor all the baby denominators.

$$\dfrac{\dfrac{x+2}{x+6} - \dfrac{x+8}{(x-2)(x+6)}}{\dfrac{x^2+11x-8}{(x-2)(x+11)} - \dfrac{x-1}{x-2}}$$

② The least common multiple of all the baby denominators is $(x+6)(x-2)(x+11)$ Multiply each term by that and cancel.

$$\dfrac{(x+2)(x-2)(x+11) - (x+8)(x+11)}{(x^2+11x-8)(x+6) - (x-1)(x+11)(x+6)}$$

Now factoring $x+11$ out of the numerator and $x+6$ out of the denominator . . .

$$= \dfrac{(x+11)(\,(x+2)(x-2) - (x+8)\,)}{(x+6)(\,(x^2+11x-8) - (x-1)(x+11)\,)}$$

$$= \dfrac{(x+11)(\,x^2-4-x-8)}{(x+6)(\,x^2+11x-8-x^2-10x+11)}$$

$$= \dfrac{(x+11)(x-4)(x+3)}{(x+6)(x+3)}$$

$$= \dfrac{(x+11)(x-4)}{x+6}$$

The Complete Solutions and Answers

2203. The sum (addition) of two negative numbers is always negative. For example, $(-5) + (-8) = -13$. One loss added to another loss always results in a loss.

2210. $-5 > \underline{\ ?\ }$ will be true for any number in the set $\{\ldots -8, -7, -6\}$. Numbers such as -9 are less than -5 since -9 is to the left of -5 on the number line.

2222. Any finite set has a cardinality that is equal to some whole number. But that is not true for infinite sets. No whole number can describe the cardinality of, for example, $\{2, 4, 6, 8, 10, 12, 14, \ldots\}$.

2226. Joe likes his cereal with exactly 8% flour in it. (The rest is sugar and artificial flavorings.) He asked Darlene take his two boxes of cereal—Captain Mousebait (7% flour) and Sergeant Sugar (11% flour)—and mix them together to get 300 ounces.

      How much of each cereal should Darlene use?

❶ Using the Let x = . . . approach:

    Let x = the number of ounces of Captain Mousebait cereal used.

    Then $300 - x$ = the number of ounces of Sergeant Sugar used.

    Then $0.07x$ = the amount of flour contributed by the Mousebait.

    Then $0.11(300 - x)$ = the amount of flour contributed by the Sergeant Sugar cereal.

    Finally, since Joe wants 24 (= 8% of 300) ounces of flour in the final mixture, we have the equation: $\quad 0.07x + 0.11(300 - x) = 24$

distributive law	$0.07x + 33 - 0.11x = 24$
combine	$-0.04x + 33 = 24$
add 0.04x to both sides	$33 = 24 + 0.04x$
subtract 24 from both sides	$9 = 0.04x$
divide both sides by 0.04	$225 = x$

Darlene should use 225 ounces of Captain Mousebait and 75 ounces of Sergeant Sugar.

❷ Using Six Pretty boxes:

	flour	percent	ounces of cereal
Captain Mousebait	$0.07x$	7%	x
Sergeant Sugar	$0.11(300 - x)$	11%	$300 - x$

The Complete Solutions and Answers

2249. The diameter of a circle will always pass through the center of the circle. The definition of a diameter is a segment whose endpoints are on the circle and that passes through the center of the circle.

NONE OF THESE ARE DIAMETERS!

Endpoints not on the circle

Not a circle

Doesn't go through the center

It's not a segment

2255. Let's review the facts.

Fact #1: Every fraction can be expressed as a repeating decimal.

Fact #2: Pi can't be expressed as a repeating decimal.

Conclusion: Pi can't be expressed as a fraction.

(This is called logic. Many colleges offer math courses in logic.)

2258. Joe decided one night to read "In the Clearing." He first read the poem at the rate of 40 words/minute. Then he decided to read it backwards. Reading backwards slowed his reading rate down to 5 words/minute.

It took him a total of 27 minutes to read the poem in both directions. How long did it take Joe to read the poem in the normal direction?

❶ Using the Let t = . . . approach:

Let t = the number of minutes it took Joe to read "In the Clearing" in the normal direction.

Then 27 − t = the number of minutes to read the poem backwards.

Then 40t = the number of words in the poem.

Then 5(27 − t) = the number of words in the poem.

Finally, the equation is

$$40t = 5(27 - t)$$
$$40t = 135 - 5t$$
$$45t = 135$$
$$t = 3$$

It took Joe 3 minutes to read the poem in the normal direction

❷ Using the Six Pretty boxes approach:

	words read	words/minute	time spend reading
reading forwards	40t	40	t
reading backwards	5(27 − t)	5	27 − t

The Complete Solutions and Answers

2270. It is really easy to find a number y, such that $y \leq y$. It is always true that $y \leq y$.

2272. Joe went to buy some frogs. At Diamond Frogs he paid \$10/frog. At Hairy Frogs, he spent the same amount of money, but since the price was \$12/frog, he bought one less frog than he did at Diamond Frogs. How many frogs did he buy at Diamond Frogs?

❶ Using the Let x = . . . approach:

       Let x = the number of frogs he bought at Diamond Frogs.

       Then x – 1 = the number of frogs he bought at Hairy Frogs. (He bought one less at Hairy Frogs than he did at Diamond.)

       Then 10x = the amount spent at Diamond Frogs. (He bought x frogs at \$10/frog.)

       Then 12(x – 1) = the amount spent at Hairy Frogs. (He bought x – 1 frogs at \$12/frog.)

       Finally, since he spent the same amount at each store, we have the equation

$$
\begin{aligned}
10x &= 12(x-1) & \\
10x &= 12x - 12 & \text{distributive law}\\
10x + 12 &= 12x & \text{add 12 to both sides}\\
12 &= 2x & \text{subtract 10x from both sides}\\
6 &= x & \text{divide both sides by 2}
\end{aligned}
$$

Joe bought 6 frogs at Diamond Frogs.

❷ Using the Six Pretty Boxes approach:

	total cost	price per frog	quantity purchased
Diamond			x
Hairy			

→

	total cost	price per frog	quantity purchased
Diamond			x
Hairy			x – 1

	total cost	price per frog	quantity purchased
Diamond		10	x
Hairy		12	x – 1

→

	total cost	price per frog	quantity purchased
Diamond	10x	10	x
Hairy	12(x – 1)	12	x – 1

2275. $\underline{\quad?\quad} < -14$ will be true for –15 or –16 or –397 or –1,000,000. It is true that $-14\frac{1}{2} < 14$, but that would be an incorrect answer since the question asks for an *integer* less than –14.

The Complete Solutions and Answers

2280. Joe liked to eat jelly beans while he watched television every evening. He bought red jelly beans at a cost of $5/lb. He bought green jelly beans at $6/lb. He spent a total of $488. He bought 8 more pounds of green than of the red. How many pounds of red jelly beans did he buy?

❶ Using the Let x = . . . approach:

Let x = the number of pounds of red jelly beans purchased.

Then x + 8 = the number of pounds of green jelly beans purchased.

Then 5x = cost of the red.

Then 6(x + 8) = cost of the green.

Finally, since the total cost was $488, we have the equation:

$$5x + 6(x + 8) = 488$$
$$5x + 6x + 48 = 488$$
$$11x + 48 = 488$$
$$11x = 440$$
$$x = 40$$

Joe bought 40 pounds of red jelly beans.

❷ Using the Six Pretty boxes approach:

	cost	$/lb.	pounds
red	5x	5	x
green	6(x + 8)	6	x + 8

2284. If $7 will buy 3 pizzas, $56 will buy 24 pizzas. I am spending eight times as much money, so I will be able to buy eight times as many pizzas.

$$\frac{\$7}{3 \text{ pizzas}} = \frac{\$56}{24 \text{ pizzas}}$$

2289. If π is approximately equal to 3.14159265358979, 1000π be approximately equal to 3141.59265358979 since multiplying by a 1000 moves the decimal point three places to the right.

2291. A circle and its diameter:

The Complete Solutions and Answers

2292. $\begin{cases} 5x + 3y = 18 \\ -5x - 10y = 10 \end{cases}$

The x-terms are a lot easier to eliminate than the y-terms.

Adding the two equations we obtain: $\qquad -7y = 28$

$$y = -4$$

To get the value of x, take $y = -4$ and put that value into any equation containing both variables.

Put $y = -4$ into the second equation ($-5x - 10y = 10$) and get:

$$-5x - (10)(-4) = 10$$
$$-5x + 40 = 10$$

add −40 to both sides $\qquad -5x = -30$

divide both sides by −5 $\qquad x = 6$

The final answer is $x = 6$ and $y = -4$.

2294. Transposing the 4y $\qquad 30y + 8 = 4y + 29$

becomes either $\qquad 26y + 8 = 29$

or $\qquad 30y - 4y + 8 = 29$

2300. Solve by graphing $\begin{cases} -2x + y = 1 \\ y = -3x + 16 \end{cases}$

For the first equation . . . if we let $x = 2$, then $y = 5$

if we let $x = -3$, then $y = -5$

For the second equation . . . if we let $x = 5$, then $y = 1$

if we let $x = 2$, then $y = 10$

We estimate the point of intersection: (3, 7). Solving two equations with two unknowns by graphing gives an answer that is approximately true, depending on how carefully you do your drawing.

Why do graphing, you ask, if we can get the exact solution by elimination? Answer: Because sometimes elimination is almost impossible and graphing is the only method available.

The Complete Solutions and Answers

2301. $\sqrt{5x + 4} + 2 = x$

First step is to isolate the radical. $\qquad \sqrt{5x + 4} = x - 2$

Second step is to square both sides. $\qquad 5x + 4 = x^2 - 4x + 4$

In detail: $(x - 2)^2 = (x - 2)(x - 2) = x^2 - 2x - 2x + 4 = x^2 - 4x + 4$

Solving the equation by factoring,

we put everything on one side. $\qquad 0 = x^2 - 9x$

Factor. $\qquad 0 = x(x - 9)$

Set each factor equal to zero. $\qquad x = 0 \ \ \text{OR} \ \ x - 9 = 0$

$\qquad x = 0 \ \ \text{OR} \ \ x = 9$

Check each answer in the original equation

Checking $x = 0$
$$\sqrt{5(0) + 4} + 2 \overset{?}{=} 0$$
$$2 + 2 \overset{?}{=} 0 \ \text{No.}$$

Checking $x = 9$
$$\sqrt{5(9) + 4} + 2 \overset{?}{=} 9$$
$$7 + 2 \overset{?}{=} 9 \ \text{Yes.}$$

The final answer is $x = 9$.

2302. Solve $4x^2 + x = 6$

Put everything on one side and then we will decide whether we can solve it by factoring or by the quadratic formula. $\qquad 4x^2 + x - 6 = 0$

We will look at $b^2 - 4ac$. If it is a perfect square then the equation can be solved by factoring. $\quad b^2 - 4ac = 1 - (4)(4)(-6) = 97$.

97 is not a perfect square. Using the quadratic formula

$$x = \frac{-1 \pm \sqrt{97}}{8} \quad \text{and we're done.}$$

2303. $\qquad 3x - 7 > x - 3$

$\qquad 2x - 7 > -3 \qquad$ subtracting x from both sides

$\qquad 2x > 4 \qquad$ adding 7 to both sides

$\qquad x > 2 \qquad$ dividing both sides by 2

2304. Graph $y = 10x$ for $-5 \le x \le 5$

If $x = -5$, then $y = -50 \qquad$ plot $(-5, -50)$

If $x = -3$, then $y = -30 \qquad$ plot $(-3, -30)$

If $x = 0$, then $y = 0 \qquad$ plot $(0, 0)$

If $x = 5$, then $y = 50 \qquad$ plot $(5, 50)$

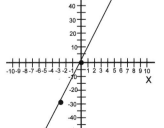

The Complete Solutions and Answers

2305. Inconsistent equations can make you rich. Let s = price of a silver coin, and let g = the price of a gold coin. Suppose one silver coin and two gold coins can be bought or sold for $1700 in New York, and can be bought or sold for $2000 in London. Show that s + 2g = 1700 and s + 2g = 2000 are inconsistent, and I will show you how to get rich.

To show that $\begin{cases} s + 2g = 1700 \\ s + 2g = 2000 \end{cases}$ is inconsistent, we multiply the top equation by –1 and add the two equations together.

The result is 0 = 300.

Now I'll show how to turn this pair of inconsistent equations into a million dollars.

Step One: How much does it cost to buy one silver coin and two gold coins in New York? Answer: $1,700.

Step Two: Take those three coins to London and sell them. How much will you receive? Answer: $2,000.

Step Three: Repeat steps one and two. Each time you will make $300. If the purchases and sales can be done by phone or on the Internet, you may be able to make $300 every couple of minutes.

Of course, after you have made enough money, you can start buying and selling six coins at a time instead of just three.

I love inconsistent equations!

2308. $3962^0 = 1$.

Anything to the zero power is equal to one.

2310. $x^4 - 16$ equals $(x^2 + 4)(x^2 - 4)$, but we are not done.
$$= (x^2 + 4)(x + 2)(x - 2)$$

2323. Solve $z^2 = 1$

$z = \pm 1$ There are almost always two solutions to pure quadratic equations.

2340. It's true that it took about three times as long to solve $x^2 + 5x - 36 = 0$ by completing the square as it did by factoring. Therefore, whenever you can solve a quadratic equation by factoring, you should do it that way. But most quadratic equations can't be factored. For example, $34823x^2 + 887x - 13 = 0$ doesn't factor. Hence, completing the square becomes useful when factoring doesn't work.

The Complete Solutions and Answers

2390. $w^4 - 81 = (w^2 + 9)(w^2 - 9)$
$\qquad\qquad\quad = (w^2 + 9)(w + 3)(w - 3)$

2400. As a decimal: $10^{-3} = \dfrac{1}{10^3} = 0.001$

2403. Joe can paint a room in 5 hours. Darlene could paint the same room in 3 hours. How long would it take to paint the room if they worked together?

This is called a "job problem."

In almost every word problem, you begin by "Let x = . . . " the thing you are trying to find out.

Let x = the number of hours for them to paint the room.

In job problems, the idea is to think of **How much of the total job can be done in one hour.** (That is the secret.)

Since Joe can do the whole job in 5 hours, he can do $\dfrac{1}{5}$ of the job in one hour.

Since Darlene can do the whole job in 3 hours, she can do $\dfrac{1}{3}$ of the job in one hour.

Since, together, they can do the whole job in x hours, they can do $\dfrac{1}{x}$ of the job in one hour.

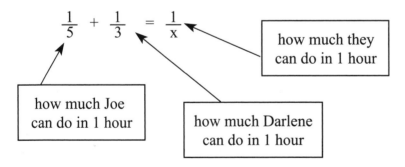

$$\dfrac{1}{5} + \dfrac{1}{3} = \dfrac{1}{x}$$

how much they can do in 1 hour

how much Joe can do in 1 hour

how much Darlene can do in 1 hour

Eliminate the fractions by multiplying through by 15x.

$$\dfrac{1(15x)}{5} + \dfrac{1(15x)}{3} = \dfrac{(15x)}{x}$$

$$3x + 5x = 15$$
$$8x = 15$$
$$x = \dfrac{15}{8} = 1\dfrac{7}{8}\ \text{hours.}$$

The Complete Solutions and Answers

2407. There is only one pure quadratic equation that had exactly one solution. It is $x^2 = 0$. Its solution is $x = 0$. It has only one solution since +0 and –0 are both the same as zero.

2410. Solve $x^2 + 4x - 7 = 0$ by completing the square.
① First step. Make sure the coefficient of the x^2 term is 1. That's already true. (If we had, for example, $8x^2$, we would have divided everything by 8.)
② Second step. Move the –7 to the right side. $x^2 + 4x = 7$
③ Complete the square. $x^2 + 4x + 4 = 7 + 4$
Review: Half of +4 is +2. We square the +2 and get 4, which we add to both sides of the equation.
④ Factor the left side. Combine the right side. $(x + 2)^2 = 11$
⑤ Take the square root of both sides.
Add a ± to the right side. $x + 2 = \pm \sqrt{11}$
⑥ Transpose the +2. $x = -2 \pm \sqrt{11}$
The answer can be written as $x = -2 \pm \sqrt{11}$
          or as $x = -2 + \sqrt{11}$ OR $-2 - \sqrt{11}$.

2444. $\dfrac{5}{0.001}$ is larger. It is equal to 5,000.

Note that $\dfrac{5}{0.0000001}$ is even larger. It is equal to 50,000,000.

2500. Simplifying $(\frac{1}{3})^{-3} = \dfrac{1}{(\frac{1}{3})^3} = 1 \div (\frac{1}{3})^3 = 1 \times \dfrac{27}{1} = 27$

2504. $(w^4 + 5)(w^3 - 7) = w^7 - 7w^4 + 5w^3 - 35$

2506. Factor $z^4 + 16$. It doesn't factor. There is no common factor, which everyone knows is the first kind of factoring that you look for, and it is not a *difference* of squares.

     The *sum* of squares does not factor. Why? Because no one has ever found a way to factor it.

2507. $C = \pi d$, where C is circumference and d is diameter. If the circumference is 4 feet, $C = \pi d$ becomes $4 = \pi d$.
     Divide both sides by π and we get $\dfrac{4}{\pi} = d$.
     The diameter is equal to $\dfrac{4}{\pi}$ feet.

The Complete Solutions and Answers

2508. $$\dfrac{\dfrac{3x^2 + 22x - 16}{x + 7}}{\dfrac{x^2 - 49}{x^2 + 11x + 24}}$$

This is the easier kind of complex fraction—one fraction divided by another. So we rewrite it using the ÷ symbol.

$$\frac{3x^2 + 22x - 16}{x + 7} \div \frac{x^2 - 49}{x^2 + 11x + 24}$$

Invert and multiply. $\dfrac{3x^2 + 22x - 16}{x + 7} \times \dfrac{x^2 + 11x + 24}{x^2 - 49}$

To multiply fractions, you multiply top times top and bottom times bottom.

$$\frac{(3x^2 + 22x - 16)(x^2 + 11x + 24)}{(x + 7)(x^2 - 49)}$$

Simplify: Factor top.
Factor bottom.

$$\frac{(3x - 2)(x + 8)(x + 8)(x + 3)}{(x + 7)(x + 7)(x - 7)}$$

Cancel like Factors.   (Nothing cancels.)

2511. Consider the line that passes through (–5, 23) and (–3, –4).

A) What is the change in y? (the rise) The change from 23 to –4 is –27.

B) What is the change is x? (the run) The change from –5 to –3 is +2.

C) What is the slope of this line? The slope is $\dfrac{-27}{2}$

2522. $\sqrt{6} + \sqrt{54} + \sqrt{8}$
$= \sqrt{6} + \sqrt{9}\sqrt{6} + \sqrt{4}\sqrt{2}$
$= \sqrt{6} + 3\sqrt{6} + 2\sqrt{2}$
$= 4\sqrt{6} + 2\sqrt{2}$

2525.

$$10x + 8 \le 22x$$

$$8 \le 12x \qquad \text{subtract } 10x \text{ from both sides}$$

$$\frac{8}{12} \le x \qquad \text{divide both sides by 12}$$

$$\frac{2}{3} \le x \qquad \text{simplifying}$$

The Complete Solutions and Answers

2527. Graph $y = (4/3)x - 3$
This is in the $y = mx + b$ (slope-intercept) form. The y intercept is -3.
The slope is $4/3$.

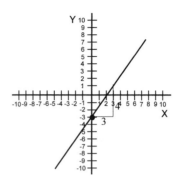

2539.
$$\frac{\dfrac{4}{y-2} + \dfrac{y^2 + 6y + 41}{y^2 - 7y + 10}}{\dfrac{y^2 + 6y + 11}{y^2 + 4y - 12} + \dfrac{2}{y+6}}$$

① Factor all the baby denominators.

$$\frac{\dfrac{4}{y-2} + \dfrac{y^2 + 6y + 41}{(y-2)(y-5)}}{\dfrac{y^2 + 6y + 11}{(y+6)(y-2)} + \dfrac{2}{y+6}}$$

② The least common multiple of all the baby denominators is $(y-2)(y-5)(y+6)$. Multiply each term by that and cancel.

$$\frac{4(y-5)(y+6) + (y^2 + 6y + 41)(y+6)}{(y^2 + 6y + 11)(y-5) + 2(y-2)(y-5)}$$

Factoring $(y+6)$ out of the top and $(y-5)$ out of the bottom . . .

$$\frac{(y+6)(\,4(y-5) + y^2 + 6y + 41\,)}{(y-5)(\,y^2 + 6y + 11 + 2(y-2)\,)} = \frac{(y+6)(y^2 + 10y + 21)}{(y-5)(y^2 + 8y + 7)}$$

$$= \frac{(y+6)(y+3)(y+7)}{(y-5)(y+7)(y+1)}$$

$$= \frac{(y+6)(y+3)}{(y-5)(y+1)}$$

The Complete Solutions and Answers

2566. Solve $\dfrac{x+13}{x^2-29} = 1$

Multiply every term by x^2-29 $x+13 = x^2-29$

Transpose everything to one side $0 = x^2-x-42$

Two numbers that multiply to -42 and add to -1.

$$0 = (x-7)(x+6)$$
$$x-7=0 \;\; \text{OR} \;\; x+6=0$$
$$x=7 \;\; \text{OR} \;\; x=-6$$

Rule: If you multiply an equation by an expression containing a variable, you must check you answer(s) back in the original problem.

checking $x=7$	checking $x=-6$
$\dfrac{20}{49-29} \overset{?}{=} 1$ yes	$\dfrac{-6+13}{36-29} \overset{?}{=} 1$ yes

The final answer is $x=7$ or $x=-6$.

2570. Solve $5x^2 = 500$

First, divide both sides by 5 $x^2 = 100$

Then $x = \pm 10$

2575. Solve $3x^2 + 6x - 23 = 0$ by completing the square.

① Divide both sides of the equation by 3 in order to make the coefficient of the x^2 term equal to 1. $x^2 + 2x - \dfrac{23}{3} = 0$

Review: 0 divided by 3 is 0.

② Transpose the $-\dfrac{23}{3}$ to the right side of the equation. $x^2 + 2x = \dfrac{23}{3}$

③ Complete the square. $x^2 + 2x + 1 = \dfrac{23}{3} + 1$

Review: Half of $+2$ is $+1$. Square $+1$ and add to both sides.

④ Factor the left. Combine the right side. $(x+1)^2 = \dfrac{26}{3}$

Review: $\dfrac{23}{3} + 1 = \dfrac{23}{3} + \dfrac{3}{3} = \dfrac{23+3}{3}$

⑤ Square root both sides and insert $\pm$. $x+1 = \pm\sqrt{\dfrac{26}{3}}$

⑥ Transpose the $+1$. $x = -1 \pm \sqrt{\dfrac{26}{3}}$ (See next problem to simplify.)

The Complete Solutions and Answers

2603. Simplifying $\left(\frac{5}{6}\right)^{-2} = \dfrac{1}{\left(\frac{5}{6}\right)^2} = 1 \div \frac{25}{36} = 1 \times \frac{36}{25} = \frac{36}{25}$

which could be expressed as $1\frac{11}{25}$

2606. $(3x + 4y)(5x + 8y) = 15x^2 + 24xy + 20xy + 32y^2$
$$= 15x^2 + 44xy + 32y^2$$

2608. Factor $6x^2 + 3xw + 8x + 4w$. When there are four (or more) terms, that is a hint that you may be factoring by grouping.

Of course, before you try to factor by grouping, you look to see whether there is a common factor. Is there something that divides into $6x^2$ and into $3xw$ and into $8x$ and into $4w$? No.

To do factoring by grouping . . .
you put the first two terms
together and find a common factor
$6x^2 + 3xw = 3x(2x + w)$

then you put the last terms together
and find a common factor
$8x + 4w = 4(2x + w)$

Then you put
them back together: $3x(2x + w) + 4(2x + w)$
It is now a binomial (has two terms).
You factor the $(2x + w)$ out of each term:
$$= (2x + w)(3x + 4) \quad \text{and you're done.}$$

2611. In a right triangle, the hypotenuse is equal to 9, and one leg is equal to 4. What is the length of the other leg?
By the Pythagorean theorem, $4^2 + x^2 = 9^2$

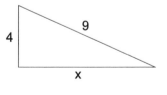

$$16 + x^2 = 81$$
$$x^2 = 65$$
$$x = \pm\sqrt{65}$$

Since a length can not be negative, we discard $x = -\sqrt{65}$.
The final answer is $x = \sqrt{65}$.

The Complete Solutions and Answers

2615.
$$-1 \pm \sqrt{\frac{26}{3}}$$

$$= -1 \pm \frac{\sqrt{26}}{\sqrt{3}} \qquad \text{Since } \sqrt{\frac{a}{b}} = \frac{\sqrt{a}}{\sqrt{b}}$$

$$= -1 \pm \frac{\sqrt{26}\,\sqrt{3}}{\sqrt{3}\,\sqrt{3}} \qquad \text{Rationalizing the denominator}$$

$$= -1 \pm \frac{\sqrt{78}}{3} \qquad \text{Since } \sqrt{a}\,\sqrt{b} = \sqrt{ab}$$

$$= \frac{-3}{3} \pm \frac{\sqrt{78}}{3}$$

$$= \frac{-3 \pm \sqrt{78}}{3}$$

2630. Solve $4x^2 + 3x - 2 = 0$ by completing the square.

① Divide through by 4. $\qquad x^2 + \frac{3}{4}x - \frac{1}{2} = 0$

② Transpose the number to the right side. $x^2 + \frac{3}{4}x = \frac{1}{2}$

③ Complete the square. $\qquad\qquad\qquad x^2 + \frac{3}{4}x + \frac{9}{64} = \frac{1}{2} + \frac{9}{64}$
Review: Half of $\frac{3}{4}$ is $\frac{3}{8}$. Squaring $\frac{3}{8}$ we get $\frac{9}{64}$.

④ Factor the left side. Add the right side. $\qquad (x + \frac{3}{8})^2 = \frac{41}{64}$

Review: $\frac{1}{2} + \frac{9}{64} = \frac{32}{64} + \frac{9}{64} = \frac{41}{64}$

⑤ Square root both sides and add $\pm$ $\qquad x + \frac{3}{8} = \pm\sqrt{\frac{41}{64}}$

$$x + \frac{3}{8} = \pm \frac{\sqrt{41}}{8}$$

$$x = \frac{-3}{8} \pm \frac{\sqrt{41}}{8}$$

$$x = \frac{-3 \pm \sqrt{41}}{8}$$

2634. 38/233 expressed as a ratio is 38:233.

2635. Dividing both sides of $-5x \geq 30$ by -5, we obtain $x \leq -6$.

The Complete Solutions and Answers

2717. A cube that is 3 feet on each edge has a volume of $(3 \text{ feet})^3$ or 27 cubic feet. The formula for the volume of a cube is $V = s^3$.

The formula for the volume of a rectangular parallelepiped (which some people call a cube) is abc. When you say *a cube of butter* everyone knows you mean a rectangular parallelepiped of butter.

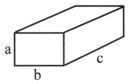

2727. Solve $\dfrac{2}{y + 2} + \dfrac{1}{y + 5} = \dfrac{21}{y^2 + 7y + 10}$

First, we factor each denominator.
$$\frac{2}{y + 2} + \frac{1}{y + 5} = \frac{21}{(y + 2)(y + 5)}$$

The smallest expression that each denominator will divide evenly into is $(y + 2)(y + 5)$.

Multiplying each term by $(y + 2)(y + 5)$
$$\frac{(2)(y + 2)(y + 5)}{y + 2} + \frac{(1)(y + 2)(y + 5)}{y + 5} = \frac{(21)(y + 2)(y + 5)}{(y + 2)(y + 5)}$$

No fractions.
$$2(y + 5) + y + 2 = 21$$
$$2y + 10 + y + 2 = 21$$
$$3y = 9$$
$$y = 3$$

Rule: If you multiply an equation by an expression containing a variable, you must check you answer(s) back in the original problem.

Checking $y = 3$.
$$\frac{2}{3 + 2} + \frac{1}{3 + 5} \overset{?}{=} \frac{21}{9 + 7(3) + 10}$$
$$\frac{2}{5} + \frac{1}{8} \overset{?}{=} \frac{21}{40}$$
$$\frac{16}{40} + \frac{5}{40} \overset{?}{=} \frac{21}{40} \qquad \text{yes}$$

The final answer is $y = 3$.

2745. Simplify $\dfrac{w^{-5} + w^7 x^{-2}}{w^{30} x^{40}}$

Multiplying top and bottom by $w^5 x^2$, will eliminate all the negative exponents.
$$\frac{(w^{-5} + w^7 x^{-2}) w^5 x^2}{w^{30} x^{40} w^5 x^2} = \frac{x^2 + w^{12}}{w^{35} x^{42}}$$

The Complete Solutions and Answers

2777. If the graph of $y = 3x^5 - 0.07x + 1$ passes through the origin, then $(0, 0)$ must satisfy the equation. Putting $x = 0$ and $y = 0$ into the equation, we obtain: $0 = 3(0^5) - 0.07(0) + 1$, which is $0 = 1$. Since this is not true, the graph does not pass through the origin.

2788. The formula for the volume of a sphere is $(4/3)\pi r^3$ where r is the radius. The volume of a sphere that has a radius of 5 inches is equal to

$(4/3)\pi r^3 \approx (4/3)(3)(5^3) = \dfrac{(4)(3)(125)}{3} = 500$ cubic inches.

2790. $(2x + 5y)(3x + 4y + 10z)$

$= 6x^2 + 8xy + 20xz + 15xy + 20y^2 + 50yz$

$= 6x^2 + 23xy + 20xz + 20y^2 + 50yz$

2800. Factor $x^3 - 5x^2 + 4x - 20$.

First you check for a common factor of all four terms. There isn't any.
Then you pull the common
factor out of the first two
terms: $x^2(x - 5)$

Then you pull the common factor out of the
last two terms: $4(x - 5)$

Then you put
them back together: $x^2(x - 5) + 4(x - 5)$
and factor the $(x - 5)$
out of the two terms: $(x - 5)(x^2 + 4)$

2888. To convert $\dfrac{37}{123}$ into a repeating decimal just divide $123\overline{)37.000...}$

until it starts to repeat. In case you are curious, when you divide, you'll get $0.30081300813008130081300813....$

2890. $\sqrt[3]{1000} = 10$ since $10^3 = 1000$

The Complete Solutions and Answers

2892. Joe decided he was going to try to do some cooking. One Tuesday he cooked up a big batch of baloney sauce. It was 20% fat (by weight). On Wednesday he cooked up a batch of yam sauce with extra bacon grease. It was 60% fat (by weight).

On Thursday he mixed the two sauces together and found that he had 100 pounds of Joe's Super Sauce that was 50% fat. How much baloney sauce had gone into the mixture?

① Using the "Let x = . . . " approach:

Let x = the number of pounds of baloney sauce Joe made.

Then 100 – x = the number of pounds of yam sauce he made.

Then 0.2x = the pounds of fat contributed by the baloney sauce. (There were x pounds of baloney sauce and it was 20% fat.)

Then 0.6(100 – x) = the number of pounds of fat contributed by the yam sauce. (There were 100 – x pounds of yam sauce and it was 60% fat.)

0.5(100) = the number of pounds of fat in Joe's Super Sauce final mixture. (There were 100 pounds, and it was 50% fat.)

$$0.2x + 0.6(100 - x) = 0.5(100)$$
$$0.2x + 60 - 0.6x = 50$$
$$-0.4x + 60 = 50$$
$$10 = 0.4x$$

Dividing both sides by 0.4 $25 = x$

Joe used 25 pounds of baloney sauce.

② Using Six Pretty boxes . . .

	lbs. of fat	%	lbs. of sauce
baloney sauce	0.2x	20%	x
yam sauce	0.6(100 – x)	60%	100 – x

2894. Graph the line that passes through (1, –6) that has a slope of $\frac{9}{2}$

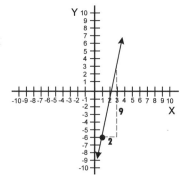

2896. Multiplying both sides of $-16 \le -x$ by -1, we have $16 \ge x$, which can also be expressed as $x \le 16$.

The Complete Solutions and Answers

2898. The coefficient of 6xyz is 6. The coefficient is the number that comes in front of the letter(s). If there is no number (such as in xyz), then think of xyz as 1xyz.

2900. Alexander and Betty went to a drive-in movie where they were offered Giggle Meals. Each meal consisted of one french fry (worth 5¢), one tiny drink (worth 7¢), and one ounce of french fry sauce (worth 4¢).

One Giggle Meal would hardly be enough to feed either of them. They bought a lot of those meals. The bill was $3.68. How many Giggle Meals did they buy?

❶ Using the Let n = . . . approach:

Let n = the number of Giggle Meals they bought.

Then 5n = the cost of the french fries in cents they bought. (They bought n french fries that were each worth 5¢)

Then 7n = the cost of the tiny drinks in cents that they bought.

Then 4n = the cost in cents of the french fry sauces they bought.

Finally, since the cost in cents of the french fries, the drinks, and the sauces added up to 368¢, we have the equation: $5n + 7n + 4n = 368$ (Note that we work in cents throughout. You can't have the left side of the equation in cents and the right side in dollars.)

adding $\qquad 16n = 368$

dividing both sides by 16 $\qquad n = 23$

They bought 23 Giggle Meals.

❷ Using Nine Pretty Boxes approach:

	total bill	price per Giggle Meal	quantity of meals purchased
french fries			n
drinks			
sauces			

→

	total bill	price per Giggle Meal	quantity of meals purchased
french fries			n
drinks			n
sauces			n

	total bill	price per Giggle Meal	quantity of meals purchased
french fries		5	n
drinks		7	n
sauces		4	n

→

	total bill	price per Giggle Meal	quantity of meals purchased
french fries	5n	5	n
drinks	7n	7	n
sauces	4n	4	n

The Complete Solutions and Answers

2901. Transpose the variables to the left side and the numbers to the right side: $50w + 3 = 11 - w$ becomes

either $\quad$ $51w = 8$ $\qquad$ if you combine terms

or $\quad$ $50w + w = 11 - 3$ $\qquad$ if you don't combine terms

2904. $\begin{cases} 10x + 6y = 62 \\ 8x - 2y = 2 \end{cases}$

Add these two equations, neither variable disappears. Instead multiply the second equation by 3 and get:

$\begin{cases} 10x + 6y = 62 \\ 24x - 6y = 6 \end{cases}$

(This is a little like getting a common denominator to add fractions. If you were adding $\frac{1}{6}$ and $\frac{1}{2}$ you would made them both into sixths: $\frac{1}{6}$ and $\frac{3}{6}$)

Now add the two equations, the y-terms disappear.

$34x = 68$

$\quad x = 2$

To obtain the value of y, substitute $x = 2$ into any equation that contains both variables. Put $x = 2$ into the first equation $(10x + 6y = 62)$ and obtain: $\quad 20 + 6y = 62$

$\qquad\qquad\qquad 6y = 42 \qquad$ subtracting 20 from both sides

$\qquad\qquad\qquad\ y = 7 \qquad$ dividing both sides by 6

The final answer is $x = 2$ and $y = 7$.

2909. Solve by graphing $\qquad \begin{cases} y = 3x + 5 \\ 4x + y = -15 \end{cases}$

For the first equation . . . $\qquad$ if $x = 0$, then $y = 5$ $\quad$ plot $(0, 5)$

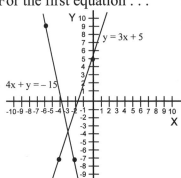

if $x = -4$, then $y = -7$ $\quad$ plot $(-4, -7)$

For the second equation . . .

if $x = -2$, then $y = -7$ $\quad$ plot $(-2, -7)$

if $x = -6$, then $y = 9$ $\quad$ plot $(-6, 9)$

The lines intersect at about $(-3, -4)$.

156

The Complete Solutions and Answers

2930. For every 157 miles I jog, I lose 3 pounds. The ratio of miles to pounds to 157:3.

2935.
$$\begin{cases} 5x + 2y = -6 \\ 6x + 5y = 11 \end{cases}$$

The numbers will be easier if we eliminate the y variable.

Multiply the first equation by 5 and the second equation by –2.

$$\begin{cases} 25x + 10y = -30 \\ -12x - 10y = -22 \end{cases}$$

Add the equations together: $13x = -52$

$$x = -4$$

Substituting $x = -4$ into the second equation

$$6(-4) + 5y = 11$$
$$-24 + 5y = 11$$
$$5y = 35$$
$$y = 7$$

The solution is $x = -4$ and $y = 7$.

2939. You multiply together nine numbers. No two of them are equal. The answer is equal to zero. Three of the numbers are positive. How many are negative?

We know that at least one of the numbers must be equal to zero since if you multiply numbers, the only time you get an answer of zero is when at least one of the numbers is zero.

We are told that no two of the numbers are equal. Therefore, exactly one of the nine numbers is zero.

Of the nine numbers, one is zero, three are positive. That means that the other five numbers must be negative.

2941. Let x = the Calories that one pullup takes. $\begin{cases} x + 3y = 25 \\ 3x + 2y = 33 \end{cases}$
Let y = the Calories that one pushup takes.

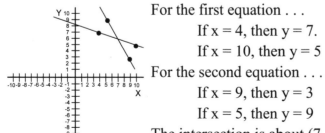

For the first equation . . .

If x = 4, then y = 7.   plot (4, 7)

If x = 10, then y = 5   plot (10, 5)

For the second equation . . .

If x = 9, then y = 3   plot (9, 3)

If x = 5, then y = 9   plot (5, 9)

The intersection is about (7, 6).

Pull ups take 7 Calories. Pushups take 6.

The Complete Solutions and Answers

2943. A sphere that has a diameter of 8 miles has a radius of 4 miles.
Its exact volume is $(4/3)\pi r^3 = (4/3)\pi 4^3 = 256\pi/3$ cubic miles.
Since the question asks for the *exact* volume, we can not approximate π by
3 or by 3.1416 or by $\frac{22}{7}$.

2946. $(x + y)(x + 2y) = x^2 + 2xy + xy + 2y^2 = x^2 + 3xy + 2y^2$.

2949. Factor $2x^2y - 10x^2w - 7y + 35w$

There is no common factor of all four terms. (We always look for a common factor first.)
We group the first two terms
and factor: $2x^2(y - 5w)$ and factor the last two terms:
$$-7(y - 5w)$$

and put them back together:
$2x^2(y - 5w) - 7(y - 5w)$
and factor out $(y - 5w)$
and get $(y - 5w)(2x^2 - 7)$

> Note that if I had factored out a 7 instead of a –7,
> I would have 7(–y + 5w)
> and that wouldn't work when I put them back
> together.

2950. Simplify $\dfrac{x^2 - 81}{x + 9}$

To simplify a fraction, you ① factor the top;

② factor the bottom; and

③ cancel like factors.

$$\frac{x^2 - 81}{x + 9} = \frac{(x + 9)(x - 9)}{x + 9} = x - 9$$

2954. $\dfrac{2}{x^2 - 2x - 15} + \dfrac{7}{x^2 - 13x + 40}$

First, factor the denominators $\dfrac{2}{(x + 3)(x - 5)} + \dfrac{7}{(x - 5)(x - 8)}$

Interior decoration $\dfrac{2(x - 8)}{(x + 3)(x - 5)(x - 8)} + \dfrac{7(x + 3)}{(x - 5)(x - 8)(x + 3)}$

Add $\dfrac{2(x - 8) + 7(x + 3)}{(x + 3)(x - 5)(x - 8)}$

Distributive property $\dfrac{2x - 16 + 7x + 21}{(x + 3)(x - 5)(x - 8)}$ which is $\dfrac{9x + 5}{(x + 3)(x - 5)(x - 8)}$

And this can't be simplified any further.

The Complete Solutions and Answers

2960. Alexander can unload a boxcar full of books in 2 days. Betty can unload it in 3 days. It takes Joe 20 days to unload the boxcar.

      If all three work together, how long would it take them to unload a boxcar full of books?

    Let x = the number of days it would take them to unload the boxcar.

    Remember, for job problems, the secret is **How much of the total job can be done in one day**—or in one week or one century or one second—depending on the units of time being used.

    Alexander can do the whole job by himself in 2 days. Therefore, he can do $\frac{1}{2}$ of the job in one day.

    Betty can do the whole job by herself in 3 days. Therefore, she can do $\frac{1}{3}$ of the job in one day.

    Joe can do $\frac{1}{20}$ of the whole job in one day.

    Together, they can do $\frac{1}{x}$ of the job in one day.

$$\frac{1}{2} + \frac{1}{3} + \frac{1}{20} = \frac{1}{x}$$

The least common multiple of 2, 3, 20 and x is 60x. That's the smallest number that 2, 3, 10, and x can evenly divide into.

Multiplying each term by 60x
$$\frac{1(60x)}{2} + \frac{1(60x)}{3} + \frac{1(60x)}{20} = \frac{60x}{x}$$
$$30x + 20x + 3x = 60$$
$$53x = 60$$
$$x = \frac{60}{53} = 1\frac{7}{53} \text{ days}$$

3000. The cardinality of {⅔} is 1, since the set contains one element.

3005. {6, 7, 123} ∪ {6, A} = {6, 7, 123, A}

    It would not be correct to write {6, 6, 7, 123, A} because you are not supposed to list the same element twice. (It makes counting the number of members of a set too hard.)

    It would have been correct to write the answer as {7, 6, 123, A} or as {6, 7, A, 123} or as {A, 123, 7, 6} because the order in which the elements of a set are listed does not matter.

The Complete Solutions and Answers

3009. Factor $x^5y^2 - 9x^5 + 3y^2 - 27$

First, we check for a common factor for all four terms. There isn't any.

Group the first two
and factor: $x^5(y^2 - 9)$

Group the last two
and factor: $3(y^2 - 9)$

Put them together
$x^5(y^2 - 9) + 3(y^2 - 9)$
and factor out the $(y^2 - 9)$: $(y^2 - 9)(x^5 + 3)$
Wait! We are not done. There's a difference of squares.

$= (y + 3)(y - 3)(x^5 + 3)$ Now we're done.

3012. To simplify $\sqrt{27}$ we use the rule $\sqrt{ab} = \sqrt{a}\sqrt{b}$. What we want happen is that a is a perfect square (such as 4, 9, 16, 25, 36, 49, 64. . .). $\sqrt{27} = \sqrt{9}\sqrt{3} = 3\sqrt{3}$

Note: We like to write $3\sqrt{3}$ rather than $\sqrt{3}3$, because there is the danger that $\sqrt{3}3$ might be accidentally read as $\sqrt{33}$.

3015. $5x - 4\overline{)25x^3 + 5x^2 - 5x}$
Fill in the missing term, which
is $+ 0$ and do the division.

$$
\begin{array}{r}
5x^2 + 5x + 3 + \frac{12}{5x-4} \\
5x - 4\overline{)25x^3 + 5x^2 - 5x + 0} \\
\underline{25x^3 - 20x^2} \\
25x^2 - 5x \\
\underline{25x^2 - 20x} \\
15x + 0 \\
\underline{15x - 12} \\
12
\end{array}
$$

3020.
$$2x^2 + 75 = 5x^2$$
$$75 = 3x^2$$
$$25 = x^2$$
$$\pm 5 = x$$

The Complete Solutions and Answers

3022. Graph $y \le (4/3)x - 3$

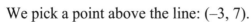

In the previous problem we graphed the line.
Now we need to test each side of the line to
determine which side to shade in.

We pick a point above the line: $(-3, 7)$.
Does that make $y \le (4/3)x - 3$ true?

$$7 \overset{?}{\le} (4/3)(-3) - 3$$
$$7 \overset{?}{\le} -4 - 3$$
$$7 \le -7 \text{ is not true. We don't shade that side.}$$

We pick a point below the line: $(6, 0)$.
Does that make $y \le (4/3)x - 3$ true?

$$0 \overset{?}{\le} (4/3)6 - 3$$
$$0 \overset{?}{\le} 8 - 3$$
$$0 \le 5 \text{ is true. We shade that side.}$$

3030. $\sqrt{6-y} + y = 0$

Isolate the radical on one side of the equation. $\quad \sqrt{6-y} = -y$
Square both sides. $\quad 6 - y = y^2$
Solve by factoring.

Put everything on one side. $\quad 0 = y^2 + y - 6$
Factor. $\quad 0 = (y-2)(y+3)$
Set each factor equal to zero. $\quad y - 2 = 0 \text{ OR } y + 3 = 0$
$$y = 2 \text{ OR } y = -3$$

Check each answer in the original equation.

$y = 2$
$\sqrt{6-2} + 2 \overset{?}{=} 0$
No.

$y = -3$
$\sqrt{6-(-3)} + (-3) \overset{?}{=} 0$
$3 \quad + (-3) \overset{?}{=} 0$
Yes.

The final answer is $y = -3$.

3037. Zero is a rational number because it can be expressed as $\frac{a}{b}$
where a and b are integers and $b \ne 0$.

Watch me do it: $0 = \frac{0}{5}$ I could also have written: $0 = \frac{0}{39836}$

161

The Complete Solutions and Answers

3114. Simplify $\dfrac{y^2 - y - 12}{y^2 - 16}$

To simplify a fraction, you ① factor the top;

② factor the bottom; and

③ cancel like factors.

$$\frac{y^2 - y - 12}{y^2 - 16} = \frac{(y+3)(y-4)}{(y+4)(y-4)} = \frac{y+3}{y+4}$$

Do not go **cancel crazy** and cancel the y's. (y is one of two terms in the numerator. y is not a factor of the numerator.)

3116. The integers = {. . . −3, −2 , −1, 0, 1, 2, . . . }.

3121. $\sqrt{300} = \sqrt{100}\,\sqrt{3} = 10\sqrt{3}$

3160. Joe bought 3 cupcakes for $14. For $140, he could buy ten times as many cupcakes. He could buy 30 cupcakes.

3162. Factor $x^2y - 2x^2 + 8xy - 16x + 15y - 30$

Grouping the

first two: $x^2(y - 2)$

Grouping the second

two: $8x(y - 2)$

Grouping the third

pair: $15(y - 2)$

Putting them together: $x^2(y - 2) + 8x(y - 2) + 15(y - 2)$

(This is now a trinomial.)

Factoring out of each term $(y - 2)$

we obtain: $(y - 2)(x^2 + 8x + 15)$

We are not done. The $x^2 + 8x + 15$ is an "easy trinomial."

To factor $x^2 + 8x + 15$, we need to find two numbers that add to 8 and multiply to 15. How about +3 and + 5?

Finally, $(y - 2)(x^2 + 8x + 15) = (y - 2)(x + 3)(x + 5)$

3170. If the radius is 6 cm, then the diameter is 12 cm. Since $C = \pi d$, where C is the circumference and d is the diameter, we obtain $C = \pi 12$.

The circumference is 12π cm.

The Complete Solutions and Answers

3209. 1000π as a decimal is just

3141.59265358979323846264338327950288419716939937510582097494459230781640628620899862803482534211706798214808651328230664709384460955058223172535940812848111745028410270193852110555964462294895493038196442881097566593344612847564823378678316527120190914564856692346034861045432664821339360726024914127372458 7...

The decimal has been moved three places to the right. Since π expressed as a decimal is non-repeating, 1000π must be non-repeating.

3211. $(a + b + c + d)(a + b + c + d)$

$= a^2 + ab + ac + ad$ the first "a" has multiplied each term in the second factor

$+ ba + b^2 + bc + bd$ the first "b" has multiplied each term in the second factor

$+ ca + cb + c^2 + cd$ the first "c" has multiplied each term in the second factor

$+ da + db + dc + d^2$ the first "d" has multiplied each term in the second factor

$= a^2 + b^2 + c^2 + d^2 + 2ab + 2ac + 2ad + 2bc + 2bd + 2cd$

3215. Factor $2wy^2 + 2wy - 60w - 3y^2 - 3y + 90$

Group the first three terms: $2w(y^2 + y - 30)$ and group the last three terms: $-3(y^2 + y - 30)$

Put them together $2w(y^2 + y - 30) - 3(y^2 + y - 30)$

Factor out the $(y^2 + y - 30)$: $(y^2 + y - 30)(2w - 3)$

We are not done.

$y^2 + y - 30$ is an "easy trinomial": we want two numbers that add to $+1$ and multiply to -30. How about -5 and $+6$?

$(y^2 + y - 30)(2w - 3) = (y - 5)(y + 6)(2w - 3)$

3222. $\dfrac{6}{x^2 + 3x} + \dfrac{5x}{x^2 - 2x - 15}$

Factor the denominators $\dfrac{6}{x(x + 3)} + \dfrac{5x}{(x + 3)(x - 5)}$

Interior decorate $\dfrac{6(x - 5)}{x(x + 3)(x - 5)} + \dfrac{5x(x)}{(x + 3)(x - 5)(x)}$

Add $\dfrac{6(x - 5) + 5x^2}{x(x + 3)(x - 5)}$

Distributive law $\dfrac{6x - 30 + 5x^2}{x(x + 3)(x - 5)}$

$5x^2 + 6x - 30$ doesn't factor, so the fraction can't be simplified.

3256. $(-5)(+2)(-7)$
$= (-10)(-7)$
$= +70$

3260. Factor $9x^4 + 54x^2 - x^2y^2 - 6y^2$
Group the first two:
$9x^2(x^2 + 6)$

Group the last two:
$y^2(-x^2 - 6)$ No. I can tell that won't work.
It doesn't match the $(x^2 + 6)$ in the first grouping.

Group the last two:
$-y^2(x^2 + 6)$

Put them together: $9x^2(x^2 + 6) - y^2(x^2 + 6)$
Factor out the $(x^2 + 6)$: $(x^2 + 6)(9x^2 - y^2)$
Are we done? No. I see a difference of squares.
$(x^2 + 6)(9x^2 - y^2) = (x^2 + 6)(3x + y)(3x - y)$

3262. Simplify $\dfrac{14x^2 + 23x + 3}{10xw + 2x + 15w + 3}$

To simplify a fraction, you ① factor the top;

② factor the bottom; and

③ cancel like factors.

$$\frac{14x^2 + 23x + 3}{10xw + 2x + 15w + 3} = \frac{(2x + 3)(7x + 1)}{(2x + 3)(5w + 1)} = \frac{7x + 1}{5w + 1}$$

Do not go cancel crazy and cancel the + 1's.
The details: The numerator was factored as a general trinomial. We found two numbers that multiply to $42x^2 (= 14x^2 \times 3)$ and that added to $23x$.
$14x^2 + 23x + 3 = 14x^2 + 21x + 2x + 3$
$= 7x(2x + 3) + 1(2x + 3)$
$= (2x + 3)(7x + 1)$
The denominator was factored by grouping.
$10xw + 2x + 15w + 3 = 2x(5w + 1) + 3(5w + 1) = (5w + 1)(2x + 3)$

The Complete Solutions and Answers

3299. $3.14159265358979 < 3.1416$ so $\pi < 3.1416$.

3302. The coefficient of $3.142857142857142857142857142d$ is $3.142857142857142857142857142$. The coefficient is the number that comes in front of the letter(s).

3303. Graph $(3, 7)$. It is in the first quadrant. QI

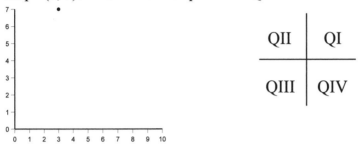

3325. A whole number x, where $x < 3$, would be either $x = 0$, $x = 1$, or $x = 2$. The whole numbers are $\{0, 1, 2, 3, 4, 5, \ldots\}$.

3328. $\{3, 4, 5\} \cup \{4, \heartsuit, w\} = \{3, 4, 5, \heartsuit, w\}$

The union of two sets is the set that contains all the elements of either set (or of both sets).

It is not correct to write $\{3, 4, 4, 5, \heartsuit, w\}$ because in listing the elements of a set inside of braces, you are not supposed to repeat the same element more than once. (One reason for this rule is that it makes it much easier to count the elements in a set if you don't repeat any of them.)

3333. Which of these are true?

$\frac{1}{2} < \frac{1}{4}$ is false. 0.5 is not less than 0.25

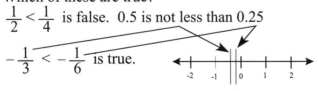

$-\frac{1}{3} < -\frac{1}{6}$ is true.

$-55 < 3$ is true. Any negative number is always less than any positive number.

$-0.01 < -0.1$ is false. -0.01 is closer to zero than -0.1 is.

3366. The volume of a pot that has a radius of 6 inches and a height of 10 inches is $\pi r^2 h = (3)(6^2)(10) = 1,080$ cubic inches.

3370. $(\sin 76° + \log 3.998 + \sqrt{888}\,)^0 = 1$

Anything raised to the zero power is equal to one.

3380. Factor $x^2y^2 - 2x^2y - 15x^2 + 8xy^2 - 16xy - 120x + 7y^2 - 14y - 105$

There is no common factor for all nine terms. (You always check for a common factor first. I might have mentioned this before.)

Group the first three terms: $x^2(y^2 - 2y - 15)$

Group the middle three terms: $8x(y^2 - 2y - 15)$

Group the last three terms: $7(y^2 - 2y - 15)$

Put them together:

$$x^2(y^2 - 2y - 15) + 8x(y^2 - 2y - 15) + 7(y^2 - 2y - 15)$$

(This is a trinomial.)

Factor out $(y^2 - 2y - 15)$: $\quad (y^2 - 2y - 15)(x^2 + 8x + 7)$

Each of these two factors, $(y^2 - 2y - 15)$ and $(x^2 + 8x + 7)$, are easy trinomials that will factor.

$$(y^2 - 2y - 15)(x^2 + 8x + 7) = (y - 5)(y + 3)(x + 1)(x + 7)$$

3393. $\dfrac{2x^2 + 19x + 48}{(x - 4)(x + 3)(x + 2)} + \dfrac{9}{x^2 - x - 12} + \dfrac{3}{x + 2}$

Factor denominators $\quad \dfrac{2x^2 + 19x + 48}{(x - 4)(x + 3)(x + 2)} + \dfrac{9}{(x - 4)(x + 3)} + \dfrac{3}{x + 2}$

Interior decorate

$$\dfrac{2x^2 + 19x + 48}{(x - 4)(x + 3)(x + 2)} + \dfrac{9(x + 2)}{(x - 4)(x + 3)(x + 2)} + \dfrac{3(x - 4)(x + 3)}{(x + 2)(x - 4)(x + 3)}$$

Add and multiply out $\quad \dfrac{2x^2 + 19x + 48 \quad + 9x + 18 \quad + 3x^2 - 3x - 36}{(x - 4)(x + 3)(x + 2)}$

Combine $\quad \dfrac{5x^2 + 25x + 30}{(x - 4)(x + 3)(x + 2)}$

Factor the top $\quad \dfrac{5(x^2 + 5x + 6)}{(x - 4)(x + 3)(x + 2)}$ ☜Always look for a common factor first.

More factoring $\quad \dfrac{5(x + 2)(x + 3)}{(x - 4)(x + 3)(x + 2)}$

Cancel like factors $\quad \dfrac{5}{x - 4}$

The Complete Solutions and Answers

3404. $(x + y)^2 = (x + y)(x + y) = x^2 + xy + xy + y^2 = x^2 + 2xy + y^2$
It does not equal $x^2 + y^2$.
There is no "distributive law of exponents over addition."

3407. Factor $3x^2 + 13x + 4$.
Find the product of $3x^2$ and 4.
We are looking for two numbers that multiply to $12x^2$ and that add to $13x$.
That would be $+12x$ and $+x$.
Split the $13x$ into $12x$ and x:
$$3x^2 + 13x + 4$$
$$3x^2 + 12x + x + 4$$

and then factor by grouping.

Factor the first two terms:
$3x(x + 4)$

Factor the last two terms:
$1(x + 4)$

Put them back together: $\quad 3x(x + 4) + 1(x + 4)$
and factor the $(x + 4)$ out: $\quad (x + 4)(3x + 1)$

3411. $\dfrac{7y^2 + 47y + 18}{(y + 2)(y + 5)(y - 1)} - \dfrac{7}{(y + 2)(y + 5)} - \dfrac{4}{y - 1}$

First, turn it into an addition problem by moving the subtraction signs.
$$\frac{7y^2 + 47y + 18}{(y + 2)(y + 5)(y - 1)} + \frac{-7}{(y + 2)(y + 5)} + \frac{-4}{y - 1}$$

Interior decoration
$$\frac{7y^2 + 47y + 18}{(y + 2)(y + 5)(y - 1)} + \frac{-7(y - 1)}{(y + 2)(y + 5)(y - 1)} + \frac{-4(y + 2)(y + 5)}{(y - 1)(y + 2)(y + 5)}$$

Add $\quad \dfrac{7y^2 + 47y + 18 - 7y + 7 - 4y^2 - 28y - 40}{(y + 2)(y + 5)(y - 1)}$

Combine like terms $\quad \dfrac{3y^2 + 12y - 15}{(y + 2)(y + 5)(y - 1)}$

Factor (common factor first!) $\quad \dfrac{3(y + 5)(y - 1)}{(y + 2)(y + 5)(y - 1)}$

Cancel like factors $\quad \dfrac{3}{y + 2}$

The Complete Solutions and Answers

3424. $\dfrac{6}{5x} + 7$

To add fractions, they both have to be fractions: $\dfrac{6}{5x} + \dfrac{7}{1}$

Then interior decoration $\dfrac{6}{5x} + \dfrac{7(5x)}{1(5x)}$

Add (since they both have the same denominator now) $\dfrac{6 + 35x}{5x}$

Since the top doesn't factor, we are done.

3430. Darlene decided to build a rowboat for Joe for his birthday. She and Betty could build it together in 3 months. Betty working alone could build it in 4 months. How long would it take Darlene to build it alone?

You almost always start a word problem by letting x equal the thing you are trying to find out.

Let x = the number of months it would take Darlene to build the rowboat alone.

Then Darlene could do $\dfrac{1}{x}$ of the job in one month.

Since Betty could build it by herself in 4 months, she could do $\dfrac{1}{4}$ of the job in one month.

Since together they could build it in 3 months, they could do $\dfrac{1}{3}$ of the job in one month.

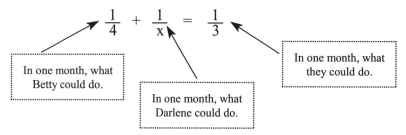

The least common multiple is 12x. We multiply each term by 12x to eliminate the denominators.

$$\dfrac{1(12x)}{4} + \dfrac{12x}{x} = \dfrac{12x}{3}$$

$$3x + 12 = 4x$$

$$12 = x \quad \text{Alone, it would take Darlene 12 months.}$$

The Complete Solutions and Answers

3502. $(a + b + c)^2 = (a + b + c)(a + b + c)$
$$= a^2 + ab + ac + ba + b^2 + bc + ca + cb + c^2$$
$$= a^2 + b^2 + c^2 + 2ab + 2ac + 2bc$$

3505. Factor $12y^2 + 51y + 45$

If you didn't look for a common factor first, this problem is pretty hard.

$12y^2 + 51y + 45 = 3(4y^2 + 17y + 15)$

(To make things easier to look at, I'm going to factor the $4y^2 + 17y + 15$ and then at the end of the problem, I'll tack the "3" back on the problem.)

Find the product of $4y^2$ and 15.

We are looking for two numbers that multiply to $60y^2$ and add to $17y$.

That would be 5y and 12y.

Split the 17y into 5y and 12y:
$$4y^2 + 17y + 15$$
$$4y^2 + 5y + 12y + 15$$

and then factor by grouping.

Factor the first two terms:

$y(4y + 5)$

Factor the second two terms:

$3(4y + 5)$

Put them back together: $\quad y(4y + 5) + 3(4y + 5)$

and factor the $(4y + 5)$ out: $\quad (4y + 5)(y + 3)$

And remember to stick the "3" back on: $\quad 3(4y + 5)(y + 3)$

3508. Simplify $\dfrac{9x^4 - y^8}{3x + y^2}$

Factor top; factor bottom; cancel like factors.

$$\frac{9x^4 - y^8}{3x + y^2} = \frac{(3x^2 + y^4)(3x^2 - y^4)}{3x + y^2}$$

Since there are no like factors, the fraction cannot be simplified.

3512. In a right triangle, the hypotenuse is equal to 9, and one leg is equal to 6. What is the length of the other leg? Simplify your answer (but do not approximate it).

By the Pythagorean theorem, $6^2 + x^2 = 9^2$

$36 + x^2 = 81 \implies x^2 = 45 \implies x = \sqrt{45} = \sqrt{9}\sqrt{5} = 3\sqrt{5}$

(We don't consider $x = -\sqrt{45}$ since we are dealing with lengths.)

The Complete Solutions and Answers

3550. Roger took his son Eddie out to practice shooting arrows. He set up a paper target to make things "realistic." Together they shot 600 arrows and 180 of them hit the target.

Six percent of Eddie's shots hit the target and 56% of Roger's hit the target.
How many arrows did Eddie shoot?

Method ① (The "Let x = . . ." approach)

Let x = the number of arrows that Eddie shot. (We always let x equal the thing we are trying to find out.)

Then 600 – x = the number of arrows that Roger shot, since together they shot 600 arrows.

Then 0.06x = the number of times Eddie hit the target. (He shot x arrows and hit the target 6% of the time.)

The 0.56(600 – x) = the number of times Roger hit the target. (He shot 600 – x arrows and hit the target 56% of the time.)

Since the number of times that Eddie hit the target plus the number of times Roger hit the target is equal to 180, we have:

$$0.06x + 0.56(600 - x) = 180$$
$$0.06x + 336 - 0.56x = 180$$
$$-0.50x + 336 = 180$$
$$156 = 0.50x$$
$$312 = x \quad \text{Eddie shot 312 arrows.}$$

Method ② Six Pretty boxes:

	no. of times target hit	%	no. of shots
Eddie	0.06x	6%	x
Roger	0.56(600 – x)	56%	600 – x

(In order to make the arithmetic easier in this problem, I wrote that they shot 600 arrows and determined that Eddie shot 312 of them. This would not be possible since 6% of 312 is 18.72, and it's difficult for 18.72 arrows to hit the target. Actually, Roger and Eddie shot 60,000 arrows over the space of several months. Eddie shot 31,200 arrows and 1872 of them hit the target.)

3555. Let x = 0.8383838383. . . .

Then 100x = 83.83838383. . . .

Subtracting the top equation from the second equation: 99x = 83

Dividing both sides by 99: $x = \dfrac{83}{99}$

The Complete Solutions and Answers

3601. $(7x + 3y)(7x - 3y) = 49x^2 - 21xy + 21xy - 9y^2$
$$= 49x^2 - 9y^2$$

Notice that two of the terms in the answer "drop out." $-21xy + 21xy = 0$

3606. Factor $5w^2 + 13w + 6$ Two that multiply to $30w^2$ and add to $13w$.

      $5w^2 + 3w + 10w + 6$

      $w(5w + 3) + 2(5w + 3)$ Factoring by grouping.

      $(5w + 3)(w + 2)$

3610. $\dfrac{x}{x + 2} + \dfrac{-12}{x^2 - 2x - 8}$

     The first step is to factor each denominator. That allows us to see what interior decorating we need to do.

$$\frac{x}{x + 2} + \frac{-12}{(x + 2)(x - 4)}$$

$$= \frac{x(x - 4)}{(x + 2)(x - 4)} + \frac{-12}{(x + 2)(x - 4)} \quad \text{☞ Doing the interior decorating}$$

$$= \frac{x(x - 4) - 12}{(x + 2)(x - 4)} \quad \text{☞ Adding the fractions}$$

$$= \frac{x^2 - 4x - 12}{(x + 2)(x - 4)} \quad \text{☞ Distributive law}$$

$$= \frac{(x + 2)(x - 6)}{(x + 2)(x - 4)} \quad \text{☞ Simplifying fractions by the famous}$$

$$= \frac{x - 6}{x - 4} \qquad \begin{array}{l}\text{three steps: A) factor top, B) factor} \\ \text{bottom, and C) cancel like factors}\end{array}$$

3620. If we have a right triangle in which the legs are 5 feet and 12 feet, how long is the hypotenuse?

By the Pythagorean theorem, $5^2 + 12^2 = x^2$

$$25 + 144 = x^2$$
$$169 = x^2$$
$$\pm 13 = x$$

     -13 doesn't make any sense for the length of anything. We throw out that answer. The length of the hypotenuse is 13 feet.

The Complete Solutions and Answers

3700. A set that has a cardinality of 7 might be:
{1, 2, 3, 4, 5, 6. 7} or {x | x is a natural number such that $80 \leq x \leq 86$} or
{α, β, γ, δ, ε, ζ, η}. Your answer may be different than mine.
(Note: {7} is not correct. The cardinality of {7} is 1.)

3705. Simplify $\dfrac{8x^2 + 2x - 15}{14x^2 + 21x}$

Factor top; factor bottom; cancel like factors.

$$\frac{8x^2 + 2x - 15}{14x^2 + 21x} = \frac{(4x - 5)(2x + 3)}{7x(2x + 3)} = \frac{4x - 5}{7x}$$

Do not go **cancel crazy** and cancel the x's.

The details: The numerator is factored as a general trinomial. We want two things that multiply to $-120x^2$ ($= 8x^2 \times -15$) and that add to $+2x$. That would be $12x$ and $-10x$.

$$8x^2 + 2x - 15 = 8x^2 + 12x - 10x - 15$$
$$= 4x(2x + 3) - 5(2x + 3)$$
$$= (2x + 3)(4x - 5) \quad \text{or, if you like, } (4x - 5)(2x + 3)$$

3716. $5\sqrt{7} + 26\sqrt{7}$ is like adding 5 apples and 26 apples. You get 31 apples.

So $5\sqrt{7} + 26\sqrt{7} = 31\sqrt{7}$.

Of course, if you want to add 4 apricots and 3 lemons, what you get is 4 apricots and 3 lemons. So $4\sqrt{a} + 3\sqrt{n} = 4\sqrt{a} + 3\sqrt{n}$. The radicands (which is the stuff under the square root sign) must be exactly alike in order to add them together.

3720. Solve $\sqrt{64 + y} - 28 = y - 20$

Isolate the radical by adding 28 to both sides. $\quad \sqrt{64 + y} = y + 8$

Square both sides. $\qquad\qquad\qquad\qquad\qquad 64 + y = y^2 + 16y + 64$

Solve by factoring. $\qquad\qquad\qquad\qquad\qquad\quad 0 = y^2 + 15y$

$$0 = y(y + 15)$$
$$y = 0 \ \text{ OR } \ y + 15 = 0$$
$$y = 0 \ \text{ OR } \ y = -15$$

$y = 0$ checks, but $y = -15$ does not check in the original equation.
The final answer is $y = 0$. -15 is an extraneous root.

The Complete Solutions and Answers

3850. $3!! = (3!)! = (3 \times 2 \times 1)! = 6! = 6 \times 5 \times 4 \times 3 \times 2 \times 1 = 720$

3855. Fill in the blank: $-54 + \underline{\hspace{1cm}} = 4$ is the same as $-54 + x = 4$.

Add 54 to both sides $x = 58$

3858. Simplify $\dfrac{w^8 - 16}{w^3 - 2w^2 + 4w - 8} = \dfrac{(w^4 + 4)(w^2 + 2)(w^2 - 2)}{(w - 2)(w^2 + 4)}$

Nothing cancels.

The details: The numerator was factored as a difference of squares.
$w^8 - 16 = (w^4 + 4)(w^4 - 4)$ which further factors again as a difference of
squares $= (w^4 + 4)(w^2 + 2)(w^2 - 2)$.

    The denominator is factored by grouping.
$w^3 - 2w^2 + 4w - 8 = w^2(w - 2) + 4(w - 2) = (w - 2)(w^2 + 4)$

3870. $\dfrac{5}{x - 7} - \dfrac{70}{x^2 - 49}$

When you are subtracting fractions, the first step is to turn it into an
addition problem. You move the subtraction sign up to the numerator of
the fraction being subtracted.

$\dfrac{5}{x - 7} - \dfrac{70}{x^2 - 49}$ becomes $\dfrac{5}{x - 7} + \dfrac{-70}{x^2 - 49}$

Then factor the denominators $\dfrac{5}{x - 7} + \dfrac{-70}{(x - 7)(x + 7)}$

Interior decoration $\dfrac{5(x + 7)}{(x - 7)(x + 7)} + \dfrac{-70}{(x - 7)(x + 7)}$

Distributive law $\dfrac{5x + 35}{(x - 7)(x + 7)} + \dfrac{-70}{(x - 7)(x + 7)}$

Add the fractions $\dfrac{5x + 35 - 70}{(x - 7)(x + 7)}$

Combine the top $\dfrac{5x - 35}{(x - 7)(x + 7)}$

Factor top, factor bottom $\dfrac{5(x - 7)}{(x - 7)(x + 7)}$

and cancel like factors $\dfrac{5}{x + 7}$

The Complete Solutions and Answers

3900. $\dfrac{4}{3x^2y^3} + \dfrac{5}{7xy^6}$

Adding and subtracting fractions is done by Interior Decoration.

You work with each fraction separately. This is different than solving fractional equations. We will not be getting rid of the fractions.

In arithmetic, when you added $\dfrac{3}{4} + \dfrac{1}{6}$ you made both fractions have the same denominators.

The common denominator will be *the smallest thing that both denominators can evenly divide into.* (That part does sound a lot like solving fractional equations.) The smallest thing that both denominators can evenly divide into is called **the least common multiple**.

In this case, the least common multiple of 4 and 6 is 12.

To do Interior Decoration we take each fraction and multiply top and bottom by something that will turn the denominator into the least common multiple.

If we were adding $\dfrac{3}{4} + \dfrac{1}{6}$ it would look like $\dfrac{3(3)}{4(3)} + \dfrac{1(2)}{6(2)}$

$$= \dfrac{9}{12} + \dfrac{2}{12} = \dfrac{11}{12}$$

$$\dfrac{4}{3x^2y^3} + \dfrac{5}{7xy^6}$$

$$= \dfrac{4(7y^3)}{3x^2y^3(7y^3)} + \dfrac{5(3x)}{7xy^6(3x)}$$

$$= \dfrac{28y^3}{21x^2y^6} + \dfrac{15x}{21x^2y^6} = \dfrac{28y^3 + 15x}{21x^2y^6}$$

After you have added fractions, you need to see if the answer can be simplified. To simplify a fraction you factor top, factor bottom and cancel like factors.

In this case, the numerator $(28y^3 + 15x)$ can't be factored. The denominator is already factored. There are no like factors to cancel.

3927. $888 + \log 7 = 888 + \log 7$ is an example of the reflexive law of equality. Any expression is equal to itself.

3955. $80 + \dfrac{2}{w} = \dfrac{80}{1} + \dfrac{2}{w} = \dfrac{80(w)}{1(w)} + \dfrac{2}{w} =$

$\dfrac{80w + 2}{w} = \dfrac{2(40w + 1)}{w}$

The Complete Solutions and Answers

3960. $\dfrac{7}{4x^{10}y^2} + \dfrac{12}{6xy^9} = \dfrac{7(3y^7)}{4x^{10}y^2(3y^7)} + \dfrac{12(2x^9)}{6xy^9(2x^9)}$

$$= \dfrac{21y^7 + 24x^9}{12x^{10}y^9}$$

$$= \dfrac{3(7y^7 + 8x^9)}{(3)(4)x^{10}y^9}$$

$$= \dfrac{7y^7 + 8x^9}{4x^{10}y^9}$$

3965. $\dfrac{x+3}{x+2} \times \dfrac{x^2-4}{x^2+5x+6}$

Multiplying fractions is a lot easier than adding them. There are no common denominators to have to figure out. You just multiply top times top and bottom times bottom.

$\dfrac{x+3}{x+2} \times \dfrac{x^2-4}{x^2+5x+6} \qquad\qquad = \dfrac{(x+3)(x^2-4)}{(x+2)(x^2+5x+6)}$

and then factor top,
factor bottom, and $\qquad\qquad = \dfrac{(x+3)(x+2)(x-2)}{(x+2)(x+2)(x+3)}$

cancel like factors $\qquad\qquad = \dfrac{x-2}{x+2}$

Please do not go cancel crazy.

You can't cancel the x's. x is not a factor of the numerator. It is a term.

You can't cancel the 2s. 2 is not a factor of the numerator. It is a term.

3979. Solve $\sqrt{13-x} - x = 7$

Add x to both sides $\qquad\qquad \sqrt{13-x} = x + 7$

Square both sides $\qquad\qquad 13 - x = x^2 + 14x + 49$

$\qquad\qquad$ Recall $(x+7)^2 = (x+7)(x+7) = x^2 + 7x + 7x + 49$

Transpose everything to the right side $\quad 0 = x^2 + 15x + 36$

Solve by factoring $\quad 0 = (x+3)(x+12) \qquad x+3=0$ OR $x+12=0$

$\qquad\qquad\qquad\qquad\qquad\qquad\qquad$ So $x = -3$ OR $x = -12$.

Checking $x = -3$ $\qquad\qquad\qquad$ Checking $x = -12$

$\sqrt{13-(-3)} - (-3) \overset{?}{=} 7 \qquad \sqrt{13-(-12)} - (-12) \overset{?}{=} 7$

Yes. $\qquad\qquad\qquad\qquad\qquad\qquad 5 + 12 \overset{?}{=} 7$ No.

-12 is an extraneous root. The final answer is $x = -3$.

The Complete Solutions and Answers

4000. Factor $8x^2 - 13x - 6$

Always check for a common factor first.
In this case, there isn't one.

We look for two numbers that multiply to $-48x^2$ and add to $-13x$.

$$8x^2 + 3x - 16x - 6$$
$$x(8x + 3) - 2(8x + 3)$$
$$(8x + 3)(x - 2)$$

4004. $\dfrac{22}{7} \approx 3.14285714285714285714285714285714571.$

Since $\pi \approx 3.14159$, it is true that $\pi < \dfrac{22}{7}$

4010. $\begin{cases} 4x + 3y = 3 \\ 12x - 7y = -71 \end{cases}$

The x-terms are a lot easier to eliminate than the y-terms.
Multiply the first equation by -3.

$$\begin{cases} -12x - 9y = -9 \\ 12x - 7y = -71 \end{cases}$$

Now, when we add the two equations, the x-terms disappear:

$$-16y = -80$$
$$y = 5 \quad \text{dividing both sides by} -16$$

Put $y = 5$ into the first equation and obtain:

$$4x + 3(5) = 3$$
$$4x + 15 = 3$$
$$4x = -12 \quad \text{subtracting 15 from both sides}$$
$$x = -3 \quad \text{dividing both sides by 4}$$

The final answer is $x = -3$ and $y = 5$.

4017. $(7x + 3y)(7x + 3y) = 49x^2 + 21xy + 21xy + 9y^2$
$$= 49x^2 + 42xy + 9y^2$$

4020. Solve $2x^2 + 7 - 5x = 7$

Putting everything on the same side
Always look for a common factor!
Set each factor equal to zero

$$2x^2 - 5x = 0$$
$$x(2x - 5) = 0$$
$$x = 0 \quad \text{OR} \quad 2x - 5 = 0$$
$$x = 0 \quad \text{OR} \quad x = 5/2$$

176

The Complete Solutions and Answers

4030. $x^2y^6 - 49$ is a difference of squares. $(xy^3 + 7)(xy^3 - 7)$

4123. The area of this trapezoid is given by the formula $A = \frac{1}{2}h(a + b)$ where h is the distance between the parallel sides a and b.

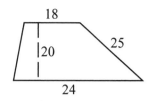

(In this problem, the 25 is irrelevant.)
$A = \frac{1}{2}(20)(18 + 24) = \frac{1}{2}(20)(42) = 420$

In the order of operations, the stuff inside parentheses is done before multiplication and division.

4125. Factor $81x^4 - 1$.   This is a difference of squares.
$\qquad (9x^2 + 1)(9x^2 - 1)$ We are not done.
$\qquad (9x^2 + 1)(3x + 1)(3x - 1)$

4127. Solve $12z^2 + 5z = 2$

Put everything on one side $12z^2 + 5z - 2 = 0$

We want two numbers that multiply
to $-24z^2$ and add to $+5z$. $8z$ and $-3z$ $12z^2 + 8z - 3z - 2 = 0$

Factor by grouping $4z(3z + 2) - (3z + 2) = 0$

$\qquad\qquad\qquad\qquad\qquad\qquad (3z + 2)(4z - 1) = 0$

Set each factor equal to zero $3z + 2 = 0$ OR $4z - 1 = 0$

$\qquad\qquad\qquad\qquad\qquad\qquad z = -2/3$ OR $z = 1/4$

4141. $7x^2 - 400 = 3x^2$
$\qquad\qquad\quad 4x^2 = 400$
$\qquad\qquad\quad\ x^2 = 100$
$\qquad\qquad\quad\ \ x = \pm10$

4150. Simplify $\sqrt{20} + \sqrt{45}$. I bet your first thought was that these can't be added since the radicands are not the same.

But first we'll simplify each square root.
$\qquad \sqrt{20} + \sqrt{45} = \sqrt{4}\sqrt{5} + \sqrt{9}\sqrt{5}$
$\qquad\qquad\qquad\quad = 2\sqrt{5} + 3\sqrt{5}$ and now they can be added
$\qquad\qquad\qquad\quad = 5\sqrt{5}$

And now you know one reason why we learned to simplify square roots: so that we might sometimes be able to add them.

The Complete Solutions and Answers

4177. The president of KITTENS University asked Betty and Darlene to make up sandwiches for everyone coming to university picnic.

If Betty worked alone, she could do it in 5 hours. Together, they can do it in 4 hours. How long would it take Darlene, if she were working alone?

Let x = the number of hours it would take Darlene to make up all the sandwiches alone.

Then $\frac{1}{x}$ = the part of the job Darlene could do in one hour.

Since Betty can do the whole job by herself in 5 hours, she can do $\frac{1}{5}$ of the job in one hour.

Since Betty and Darlene, working together, can do the whole job in 4 hours, they can do $\frac{1}{4}$ of the job in one hour.

$$\frac{1}{5} + \frac{1}{x} = \frac{1}{4}$$

The least common denominator is 20x. We multiply each term of this fractional equation by 20x to eliminate the denominators.

$$\frac{1(20x)}{5} + \frac{1(20x)}{x} = \frac{1(20x)}{4}$$

$$4x + 20 = 5x$$
$$20 = x$$

It would take Darlene 20 hours if she were working alone.

4180. Graph $y < (4/3)x - 3$

This is the same as the previous problem, except that this problem has less than (<) instead of less than or equal (≤).

With ≤ we have an equals sign, and the original line is part of the solution.

With < there is no equals sign. We don't want the line to be part of the solution. To indicate that, we make the line a dashed line.

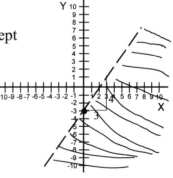

English lesson. This is a dashed line: ------------------.

This is a dotted line: ···················· .

The Complete Solutions and Answers

4260. Factor $4x^2 - 4x - 15$

Two numbers that multiply to $-60x^2$ and add to $-4x$.

$$4x^2 - 10x + 6x - 15$$
$$2x(2x - 5) + 3(2x - 5)$$
$$(2x - 5)(2x + 3)$$

4275. A **polynomial** is an expression formed by adding, subtracting, or multiplying numbers and/or letters.
55x is a polynomial because you can get it by multiplying 55 times x.
$\frac{w}{6}$ is a polynomial because you can get it by multiplying $\frac{1}{6}$ by w.

$3x^2 + 0.7y$ is a polynomial. You first multiply 3 times x times x. Then you multiply 0.7 times y. Then you add those two things together.

4278. The coefficient of x^3y^{44} is 1.
It is the same as the coefficient of $1x^3y^{44}$.

4280. $\{8\} \cup \{1, 2\} = \{8, 1, 2\}$

4282. The median average of 10, 11, 11.3, 11.7, 11.8 is the number that is in the middle of the list (assuming the numbers are arranged from smallest to largest). The median of these numbers is 11.3.

4284. Solve by elimination: $\begin{cases} 5x - 6y = 32 \\ -10x + 12y = -64 \end{cases}$

Multiply the first equation by 2: $\begin{cases} 10x - 12y = 64 \\ -10x + 12y = -64 \end{cases}$

Add the two equations: $0 = 0$.
The two equations are dependent. Any solution to either equation is a solution to the other equation. If you graphed the two equations, they would be the same line drawn twice.

4290. Factor $20z^2 + 11z - 9$

Always look for a common factor first.

$$20z^2 + 20z - 9z - 9$$

Two numbers that multiply to $-180z^2$ and add to $11z$

$$20z(z + 1) - 9(z + 1)$$
$$(z + 1)(20z - 9)$$

The Complete Solutions and Answers

4295. Solve $\begin{cases} 5x - 2y = -3 \\ 7x + 5y = -51 \end{cases}$

Multiply the first equation by 5 $\begin{cases} 25x - 10y = -15 \\ 14x + 10y = -102 \end{cases}$
Mutiply the second equation by 2

Add the equations and the y-terms drop out $\qquad 39x = -117$
Divide both sides by 39 $\qquad\qquad\qquad x = -3$

Substitute x = –3 into the first equation $\qquad 5(-3) - 2y = -3$
$$-15 - 2y = -3$$
$$-2y = 12$$
$$y = -6$$

The final answer is x = –3 and y = –6.

4300. $\qquad 6y^2 + 600 = 11y^2 - 400$
$$1000 = 5y^2$$
$$200 = y^2$$
$$\pm\sqrt{200} = y$$
$$y = \pm\sqrt{200} \qquad$$ The **symmetric law of equality**:
$$\text{If } a = b, \text{ then } b = a.$$
$$y = \pm\sqrt{100}\sqrt{2} = \pm10\sqrt{2}$$

4321. $\sqrt{63} + \sqrt{81} + \sqrt{28} \quad = \sqrt{9}\sqrt{7} + 9 + \sqrt{4}\sqrt{7}$
$$= 3\sqrt{7} + 9 + 2\sqrt{7}$$
$$= 5\sqrt{7} + 9$$
(You can't combine the $5\sqrt{7}$ and the 9.)

I take that back. You could combine $5\sqrt{7}$ and 9, but you'd get a wrong answer.

4326. The diameter of a circle is 18 inches. The circumference of a circle is equal to π times its diameter.   C = πd.
So the exactly circumference is 18π inches.

4330. Suppose you are given: 0.338338338338. . . .
Let x = 0.338338338338 . . . $\qquad$ (line 1)
Then 1000x = 338.338338338 . . . $\qquad$ (line 2)
Subtract line 1 from line 2: 999x = 338
Divide by 999: $\qquad\qquad\qquad$ x = 338/999

The Complete Solutions and Answers

4350. Factor $6y^4 + 19y^2 + 10$ *We want two numbers that multiply to $60y^4$ and that add to $19y^2$.*

$$6y^4 + 15y^2 + 4y^2 + 10$$
$$3y^2(2y^2 + 5) + 2(2y^2 + 5)$$
$$(2y^2 + 5)(3y^2 + 2)$$

4354. $(3x + 5w)^2 = (3x + 5w)(3x + 5w) = 9x^2 + 15xw + 15xw + 25w^2$
$$= 9x^2 + 30xw + 25w^2$$

4360. Solve $\dfrac{x-1}{3} - \dfrac{1}{6} = \dfrac{x-3}{2}$

To solve equations containing fractions, you multiply each term by the smallest something that every denominator divides evenly into.

    The smallest something that 3, 6, and 2 all divide evenly into is 6.

$$\frac{(x-1)\mathbf{6}}{3} - \frac{(1)\mathbf{6}}{6} = \frac{(x-3)\mathbf{6}}{2}$$

    Notice that we put parentheses around the existing numerators so that the whole numerator gets multiplied by the **6**.

    Without those parentheses, the first numerator would be $x - 1(6)$, which would be $x - 6$—and that isn't six times $x - 1$.

    Each of the denominators divides evenly into the 6.

$$(x - 1)2 - 1 = (x - 3)3 \qquad \text{No more fractions!} \ ☺$$

Distributive property $2x - 2 - 1 = 3x - 9$
$$2x - 3 = 3x - 9$$
Add 9 to both sides $2x + 6 = 3x$
Subtract 2x from both sides $6 = x$

    We do not have to check the answer because we did not multiply by an expression containing a variable.

    But I'm going to check my answer just for fun. Putting $x = 6$ into the original equation: $\dfrac{5}{3} - \dfrac{1}{6} \overset{?}{=} \dfrac{3}{2}$

Changing all the denominators to 6, we get $\dfrac{10}{6} - \dfrac{1}{6} = \dfrac{9}{6}$ which is true.

The Complete Solutions and Answers

4363.

$$\dfrac{\dfrac{12-y}{y^2-9y+20} + \dfrac{1}{y-4}}{\dfrac{2}{y+6} + \dfrac{31-2y}{y^2+y-30}}$$

① First factor all the little denominators.

$$\dfrac{\dfrac{12-y}{(y-4)(y-5)} + \dfrac{1}{y-4}}{\dfrac{2}{y+6} + \dfrac{31-2y}{(y+6)(y-5)}}$$

② Find the least common multiple of the baby denominators.
In this case, it is $(y-4)(y+6)(y-5)$

③ Multiply each term by it.

$$\dfrac{\dfrac{(12-y)(y-4)(y+6)(y-5)}{(y-4)(y-5)} + \dfrac{(y-4)(y+6)(y-5)}{y-4}}{\dfrac{(2)(y-4)(y+6)(y-5)}{y+6} + \dfrac{(31-2y)(y-4)(y+6)(y-5)}{(y+6)(y-5)}}$$

After canceling like factors, we don't have a complex fraction anymore.

$$\dfrac{(12-y)(y+6) \quad + \quad (y+6)(y-5)}{(2)(y-4)(y-5) \;+\; (31-2y)(y-4)}$$

We can factor $y+6$ out of the numerator and $y-4$ out of the denominator.

$$\dfrac{(y+6)(\,12-y \,+\, y-5\,)}{(y-4)(\,(2)(y-5)+(31-2y)\,)}$$

$$\dfrac{(y+6)(\,7\,)}{(y-4)(\,2y-10+31-2y\,)}$$

$$\dfrac{(y+6)(7)}{(y-4)(21)}$$

$$\dfrac{(y+6)}{3(y-4)}$$

The Complete Solutions and Answers

4399. Darlene can grow 50 carrots in each square meter of her garden. Joe doesn't water his garden as often as Darlene. He can grow only 40 carrots per square meter. His garden is 2 square meters larger than hers. They grow the same number of carrots. How large is her garden?

① Using the Let x = . . . approach . . .

        Let x = the size of Darlene's garden.

        Then x + 2 = the size of Joe's garden.

        Then 50x = the number of carrots that Darlene can grow.

        Then 40(x + 2) = the number of carrots that Joe can grow.

Since they can grow the same number of carrots: $50x = 40(x + 2)$

Distributive law	$50x = 40x + 80$
Subtract 40x from both sides	$10x = 80$
Divide both sides by 10	$x = 8$

Darlene's garden is 8 square meters.

② Using the Six Pretty Boxes approach . . .

	🥕	rate of production of carrots	size of garden
Darlene	50x	50 carrots/sq meter	x
Joe	40(x + 2)	40 carrots/sq meter	x + 2

4401. $\dfrac{y^2 - 1}{8} \times \dfrac{6}{(y + 1)^2} \times \dfrac{y^2 + 4y + 3}{(y - 1)^2}$

Top times top, and bottom times bottom $\quad\dfrac{(y^2 - 1)(6)(y^2 + 4y + 3)}{8(y + 1)^2(y - 1)^2}$

Factor the top. $\quad = \dfrac{(y + 1)(y - 1)(2)(3)(y + 3)(y + 1)}{(2)(2)(2)(y + 1)^2(y - 1)^2}$

Cancel like factors. $\quad = \dfrac{3(y + 3)}{4(y - 1)}$

Further explanation: In the numerator we had a y − 1, and in the denominator we had $(y - 1)^2$. That could be written as $\dfrac{y - 1}{(y - 1)(y - 1)}$ and canceling would leave $\dfrac{1}{y - 1}$

4444. If you divide two integers, the rule is:

        Signs alike ⇨ *Answer is positive.*

        Signs different ⇨ *Answer is negative.*

    It is the same rule as multiplying two integers. (We did this in *Life of Fred: Beginning Algebra Expanded Edition*.)

The Complete Solutions and Answers

4447. If (x, y) is in QII, then x must be negative and y must be positive. In symbols: $x < 0$ and $y > 0$.

QII	QI
QIII	QIV

4450. A conical party hat that is 7 inches tall and has a radius of 4 inches has a volume of $(1/3)\pi r^2 h = (1/3)(3)(4^2)(7) = 112$ cubic inches of root beer.

4466. There are many different answers possible. The number of statues you bought is proportional to:

  A) the total cost of the purchase

  B) the total weight of the statues (If you bought three times as many statues, the total weight would be three times as much.)

  C) the sales tax on the purchase (The sales tax is proportional to the purchase price.)

  D) the number of trips it would take you to haul them all out to your truck, assuming they were each so heavy that you could only carry one at a time.

  E) the number of wings (or beaks or legs)

4468. $\dfrac{100!}{99!} = 100$

Here's why: $\dfrac{100!}{99!} = \dfrac{100\times99\times98\times97\times \ldots \times3\times2\times1}{99\times98\times97\times \ldots \times3\times2\times1}$ and then cancel.

4470. x is a polynomial. It is an expression formed by combining one or more numbers and letters using only addition, subtraction, or multiplication.

0 is a polynomial. It is an expression formed by combining one or more numbers and letters using only addition, subtraction, or multiplication.

$\dfrac{w+y+2}{17}$ is a polynomial. You first add together w, y and 2, and then you multiply the result by $\dfrac{1}{17}$

$\dfrac{v}{\pi}$ is a polynomial. It is formed by multiplying v by the number $\dfrac{1}{\pi}$

$\dfrac{\pi}{v}$ is *not* a polynomial. You can't get it by multiplying numbers with letters. You would have to divide by v.

4477. Factor $2x^2 + 63x + 5$. We want two numbers that multiply to $10x^2$ and add to $63x$. I can't think of any. Truth: In real life, most trinomials chosen at random do not factor.

The Complete Solutions and Answers

4500. $\{x \mid x$ is an integer and $x > 4\}$ means $\{5, 6, 7, 8, \ldots \}$.
$\{y \mid y$ is a whole number and $y < 6\}$ means $\{0, 1, 2, 3, 4, 5\}$.
The union of these two sets is $\{0, 1, 2, 3, 4, 5, 6, \ldots \}$, which could be expressed as $\{z \mid z$ is a whole number$\}$ or in English as the set of whole numbers.

4503. In Fred's arithmetic class, he noticed that for every 8 students who used a pencil, there were 3 who used a ballpoint pen, and 1 who used a fountain pen. There were 288 students in his class. How many used ballpoint pens?

  Step One: 8:3:1

  Step Two: 8x:3x:x

  Step Three: $8x + 3x + x = 288$

  Then solve the equation: $\qquad 12x = 288$

  Divide both sides by 12 $\qquad x = 24$

The question asks for the number who use ballpoint pens. That is represented by 3x. If $x = 24$, then $3x = 72$.

  Seventy-two students use ballpoint pens.

4505. Solve $\begin{cases} 6x + 6y = -18 \\ 7x + 8y = -25 \end{cases}$

  We have two choices: (1) Eliminate the x-terms by multiplying the first equation by 7 and the second equation by –6; or (2) Eliminate the y-terms by multiplying the first equation by 4 and the second equation by –3.

  The second choice involves smaller numbers (= less work), and I choose that direction:

$$\begin{cases} 24x + 24y = -72 \\ -21x - 24y = 75 \end{cases}$$

  $3x = 3$ adding the two equations together

  $x = 1$ divide both sides by 3

Substitute $x = 1$ into the first equation: $6(1) + 6y = -18$

$6 + 6y = -18$

$6y = -24$

$y = -4$

The final answer is $x = 1$ and $y = -4$.

The Complete Solutions and Answers

4507. How many pounds of 5% bones should he mix with 8% bones to obtain 36 pounds of fish with 7% bones?

❶ Using the Let x = . . . approach:

Let x = the number of pounds of fish with 5% bones used.

Then 36 – x = the number of pounds of fish with 8% bones used.

Then 0.05x = the weight of the bones contributed by the first type of fish.

Then 0.08(36 – x) = the weight of the bones contributed by the second type of fish.

Finally, since we want 2.52 pounds of bones (7% of 36) in the final mixture, we have the equation

$$0.05x + 0.08(36 - x) = 2.52$$
$$0.05x + 2.88 - 0.08x = 2.52$$
$$-0.03x + 2.88 = 2.52$$
$$2.88 = 2.52 + 0.03x$$
$$0.36 = 0.03x$$
$$12 = x$$

He should use 12 pounds of the fish containing 5% bones.

❷ Using the Six Pretty boxes approach:

	pounds of bones	percent	pounds of fish
fish that contain fewer bones	0.05x	5	x
fish that contain more bones	0.08(36 – x)	8	36 – x

4512. If you multiply any number by zero, the answer is always zero. So 0π is the same as 0. Zero is a repeating decimal. 0 = 0.00000000000000000000000000000000000000000000000. . . .

4518. If 4 birdhouses cost $27, 8 birdhouses would cost twice as much. They would cost $54.

The Complete Solutions and Answers

4519. $\begin{cases} 6x + 3y = 6 \\ 9x + 10y = 42 \end{cases}$

Two choices: Either make the x-terms into 18x and –18x or make the y-terms into 30y and –30y. Let's choose to eliminate the x-terms. (Either choice will give the same answer.)

Multiply the first equation by 3 and the second equation by –2:

$\begin{cases} 18x + 9y = 18 \\ -18x - 20y = -84 \end{cases}$

$-11y = -66$ adding the two equations

$y = 6$

Substituting y = 6 into the first equation: $6x + 3(6) = 6$

$6x + 18 = 6$

$6x = -12$

$x = -2$

The final answer is x = –2 and y = 6.

4520.

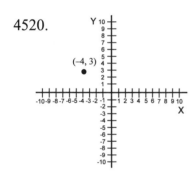

The point whose abscissa is –4 and whose ordinate is 3.

Abscissa = first coordinate = x-coordinate
Ordinate = second coordinate = y-coordinate

4522. The mean average of –8, –3, 0, 31 is found by adding up the four numbers and dividing by 4. $-8 + (-3) + 0 + 31 = 20$
20/4 = 5. The mean average is 5.

4530. $(10x^4z^5)^6 = 10^6x^{24}z^{30}$

4531. $2!!! = ((2!)!)! = (2!)! = 2! = 2$

4533. Factor $35x^2 + 13x - 4$ Multiply to $-140x^2$ and add to 13x
$35x^2 + 20x - 7x - 4$
$5x(7x + 4) - (7x + 4)$
$(7x + 4)(5x - 1)$

4535. 4xy is a monomial. It is one term.

4x + y would be a binomial.

4 + x + y would be a trinomial.

4537. Solve $\dfrac{2}{3} + \dfrac{1}{x + 7} = \dfrac{x + 15}{15}$

The smallest expression that 3, x + 7 and 15 divide into is 15(x + 7).

$$\frac{(2)\mathbf{15(x + 7)}}{3} + \frac{(1)\mathbf{15(x + 7)}}{x + 7} = \frac{(x + 15)\mathbf{15(x + 7)}}{15}$$

After canceling $\qquad (2)5(x + 7) + 15 = (x + 15)(x + 7)$

Multiplying out $\qquad\qquad 10x + 70 + 15 = x^2 + 7x + 15x + 105$

Combining $\qquad\qquad\qquad 10x + 85 = x^2 + 22x + 105$

Transposing everything $\qquad\qquad 0 = x^2 + 12x + 20$

Factoring $\qquad\qquad\qquad\qquad 0 = (x + 2)(x + 10)$

$$x + 2 = 0 \quad \text{OR} \quad x + 10 = 0$$

$$x = -2 \quad \text{OR} \quad x = -10$$

We must check both answers because we multiplied by 15(x + 7), and that is an expression containing a variable.

Checking x = –2

$$\frac{2}{3} + \frac{1}{5} \stackrel{?}{=} \frac{13}{15}$$

$$\frac{10}{15} + \frac{3}{15} \stackrel{?}{=} \frac{13}{15} \quad \text{yes}$$

Checking x = –10

$$\frac{2}{3} + \frac{1}{-3} \stackrel{?}{=} \frac{5}{15}$$

$$\frac{2}{3} - \frac{1}{3} \stackrel{?}{=} \frac{5}{15} \quad \text{yes} \qquad\qquad \text{The final answer is x = –2 or –10.}$$

4538. The square roots of 64 are 8 and –8.

4545. Simplify by rationalizing the denominator. $\dfrac{7}{\sqrt{n}}$

Multiplying top and bottom by $\sqrt{n}$ $\qquad = \dfrac{7\sqrt{n}}{\sqrt{n}\,\sqrt{n}}$

$$= \dfrac{7\sqrt{n}}{n}$$

The Complete Solutions and Answers

4580. Solve $\dfrac{1}{5x} + \dfrac{1}{2x} = \dfrac{7}{30}$

To solve equations that contain fractions, you multiply each term by something that every denominator divides evenly into.

We are looking for something that 5x, 2x, and 30 all divide into.

Their product—which is (5x)(2x)(30)—will always work, but $300x^2$ will create a lot more work than if you choose *the smallest thing that* 5x, 2x, and 30 will all divide into.

Choose 30x. It's the smallest thing that 5x, 2x, and 30 will all divide into.

We multiply each term by 30x. Consider it like a gift that Santa leaves at each house. (Translation: Multiply each numerator by 30x.)

$$\dfrac{1(\mathbf{30x})}{5x} + \dfrac{1(\mathbf{30x})}{2x} = \dfrac{7(\mathbf{30x})}{30}$$

We chose 30x because all the denominators would divide evenly into it. So the next (logical) step is to divide each denominator into the 30x:

$$6 \quad + \quad 15 \quad = \quad 7x \qquad \text{No more fractions!}$$
$$21 = 7x$$
$$3 = x$$

Rule: If you multiply an equation by an expression containing a variable, you must check you answer(s) back in the original problem.

Translation: If your gift—which was 30x in this problem—has an x in it, you must check your answer—which in this case was x = 3—back in the original equation.

Reason for the Rule: Multiplying an equation by an expression containing variables may sometimes introduce extra answers that don't work in the original equation.

Fancy words: Many textbooks call the "extra answers" **extraneous roots**.

If you say "extraneous roots" at a party where they are discussing algebra, people will think you are really smart.

Checking x = 3 in the original equation $\dfrac{1}{5x} + \dfrac{1}{2x} = \dfrac{7}{30}$

becomes $\dfrac{1}{15} + \dfrac{1}{6} \overset{?}{=} \dfrac{7}{30}$

$\dfrac{2}{30} + \dfrac{5}{30} \overset{?}{=} \dfrac{7}{30}$ Yes!

The solution is x = 3.

The Complete Solutions and Answers

4600. 7 + 5 is a polynomial with two terms.

         12 is a polynomial with one term.

A binomial is a polynomial with two terms.

A monomial is a polynomial with one term.

Easy question: Can a binomial equal a monomial?

That is the same as asking if 7 + 5 can equal 12. Easy answer: Yes.

4603. A quadratic equation is an equation with a quadratic term in it and no higher power. A quadratic term is a variable that is squared (raised to the second power).

4607. $w^2 - 3w - 18$

Two numbers that multiply to –18 and add to –3   –6 and +3

= $(w - 6)(w + 3)$

4610. Darlene's aunt is three times as old as Darlene. Twenty-one years from now, Darlene's aunt will be twice as old as Darlene will be. How old is Darlene today?

        Let d = Darlene's age today. (We usually begin by letting the variable equal the thing we are trying to find out.)

        Then 3d = Darlene's aunt's age today.

        Then d + 21 = Darlene's age 21 years from now.

        Then 3d + 21 = Darlene's aunt's age 21 years from now.

        Since in 21 years Darlene's aunt will be twice as old as Darlene, we have

$$3d + 21 = 2(d + 21)$$

Distributive law $3d + 21 = 2d + 42$

                             $d = 21$

Today, Darlene is 21 years old.

4611. The principal square root of 9 is 3. A principal square root can not be negative.

4650. Factor $8x^2 + 16x + 32$

        You always look for a common factor first.

        $8x^2 + 16x + 32 = 8(x^2 + 2x + 4)$

Can $x^2 + 2x + 4$ be factored? Can we find two numbers that add to 2 and multiply to 4? No. $8(x^2 + 2x + 4)$ is the final answer.

The Complete Solutions and Answers

4699. Solve $x^2 - 2x = 35$

First step: Transpose everything to one side of the equation.

$$x^2 - 2x - 35 = 0$$

Second step: Factor.

$$(x - 7)(x + 5) = 0 \qquad \text{Recall: Two numbers that add to } -2$$
$$\text{and multiply to } -35$$

Third step: Set each factor equal to zero and solve.

$$x - 7 = 0 \quad \text{OR} \quad x + 5 = 0$$
$$x = 7 \quad \text{OR} \qquad x = -5$$

If you like, you can check your answers to see if they are correct. If you never make errors, this checking is optional.

For fun, I'll check the $x = -5$ answer. Putting $x = -5$ into the original equation: $(-5)^2 - 2(-5) \overset{?}{=} 35$

I put a question mark over the equal sign for politeness. Until I'm done with the checking, I have to keep the question mark.

$$+25 + 10 \overset{?}{=} 35$$
$$35 = 35 \qquad \text{Yes!}$$

4700. Solve by elimination $\begin{cases} 3x + 4y = 4 \\ 4x + 5y = 6 \end{cases}$

If I eliminate the x-terms, I would make them into 12x and –12x. If I eliminate the y-terms, I would make them into 20y and –20y.

It looks like getting rid of the x-terms will be easier.

Multiply the first equation by 4 and the second equation by –3:

$$12x + 16y = 16$$
$$-12x - 15y = -18$$

Adding the two equations together: $y = -2$.

Substituting $y = -2$ into the first equation: $3x + 4(-2) = 4$
$$3x - 8 = 4$$
$$3x = 12$$
$$x = 4$$

The solution is $x = 4$ and $y = -2$.

4711. If opening your mouth and brushing your teeth are commutative, then doing things the regular way (first open mouth, then stick in the toothbrush) and doing it in reverse order (stick the brush in your mouth and then open it) would be the same.

But they aren't. Those two acts are not commutative.

The Complete Solutions and Answers

4712. A trinomial is a polynomial with three terms. Give an example of a trinomial that is equal to a monomial. How about $3 + 4 + 5 = 12$.

The whole point is that the number of terms in a polynomial is not fixed. $5xy^3 + 6xy^3$ is a binomial that is equal to $11xy^3$.

4716. Jackie is four times as old as Dale.
In $2\frac{1}{8}$ years, Jackie will be three times as old as Dale.
How old is Dale today?

Let d = Dale's age today.

Then 4d = Jackie's age today.

Then in $2\frac{1}{8}$ years Dale will be $d + 2\frac{1}{8}$ and Jackie will be $4d + 2\frac{1}{8}$

In $2\frac{1}{8}$ years, Jackie will be three times as old as Dale.

$$4d + 2\frac{1}{8} = 3(d + 2\frac{1}{8})$$

Let's do it in decimals. It will be easier to look at.

$$4d + 2.125 = 3(d + 2.125)$$
$$4d + 2.125 = 3d + 6.375$$
$$d + 2.125 = 6.375 \quad \text{subtracting 3d from both sides}$$
$$d = 4.25 \quad \text{subtracting 2.125 from both sides}$$

Dale is $4\frac{1}{4}$ years old now.

4718. Is there any situation in which a number can have more than one principal square root? No there can't be. For example, the principal square root of 100 has to be a non-negative number that when squared is equal to 100. Ten is the only possible answer.

4747. Solve $\sqrt{x + 72} - 4 = 5$

First step is to isolate the radical on one side of the equation. We add 4 to both sides. $\sqrt{x + 72} = 9$

Second step is to square both sides. $x + 72 = 81$

Subtract 72 from both sides. $x = 9$

Last step is to check the answer in the original problem. $\sqrt{9 + 72} - 4 \overset{?}{=} 5$
$$\sqrt{81} - 4 \overset{?}{=} 5$$

Yes. The answer checks. The final answer is $x = 9$.

The Complete Solutions and Answers

4811. Suppose a pizza had a diameter of 7 feet. The formula relating circumference and diameter is C = πd. So if d = 7 feet, then the exact circumference would be C = 7π feet.

4818. $\begin{cases} 3x + 4y = 4 \\ 4x + 5y = 6 \end{cases}$

For the first equation, if x = 0, then y = 1.   Plot (0, 1).

if x = –4, then y = 4.   Plot (–4, 4).

For the second equation, if x = 4, then y = –2.   Plot (4, –2).

if x = –4, then y = 4.4.   Plot (–4, 4.4).

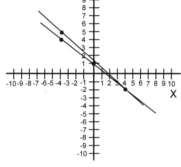

The lines intersect at about (4, –2).

4820. Joe bought a giant can of beans. Its diameter was 12 inches and its height was 10 inches. First, find the volume of that can (using 3 for π in this problem), and then convert that to quarts. (There are roughly 58 cubic inches in a quart.) Round your answer to the nearest quart.

If the diameter is 12 inches, the radius is 6 inches. The volume formula for a cylinder is V = πr²h which in this case is (3)(6²)(10) which is 1080 cubic inches.

We need to use a conversion factor (which was taught in the arithmetic books) of $\dfrac{1 \text{ quart}}{58 \text{ cubic inches}}$

$\dfrac{1080 \text{ cubic inches}}{1} \times \dfrac{1 \text{ quart}}{58 \text{ cubic inches}} \approx$ 18.62 quarts $\doteq$ 19 quarts.

≈ means "approximately equal to" $\doteq$ means "rounded to."

4822. The longest question of this book has the shortest answer. No.

4824. 20ac + 8ad + 15bc + 6bd

= 4a(5c + 2d) + 3b(5c + 2d) = (5c + 2d)(4a + 3b)

The Complete Solutions and Answers

4829. Solve $x^2 - 56 = -x$

Transpose the $-x$ so that everything is equal to zero. $x^2 + x - 56 = 0$

Factor $\quad\quad (x + 8)(x - 7) = 0$

Set each factor equal to zero $\quad\quad x + 8 = 0 \quad$ OR $\quad x - 7 = 0$

$x = -8 \quad$ OR $\quad x = 7$

4831. Factor $14x^2 + 27x - 20$

We need two numbers that multiply to $-280x^2$ and add to $+27x$.

This isn't especially easy.

If I try $20x$ and $-14x$ .... they add to $6x$. (20 and –14 are too close)

If I try $28x$ and $-10x$ .... they add to $18x$. (28 and –10 are still too close)

If I try $40x$ and $-7x$ .... they add to $33x$. (40 and –7 are too far apart)

If I try $35x$ and $-8x$ .... they add to $27x$ ☺

$$14x^2 + 27x - 20$$
$$= 14x^2 + 35x - 8x - 20 \quad\quad \text{and then we factor by grouping}$$
$$= 7x(2x + 5) - 4(2x + 5)$$
$$= (2x + 5)(7x - 4)$$

4835. If you are trying to factor a binomial—or a polynomial with any number of terms—you should always look for a common factor first.

4838.
$$\sqrt{44} + \sqrt{99} + \sqrt{11} = \sqrt{4}\sqrt{11} + \sqrt{9}\sqrt{11} + \sqrt{11}$$
$$= 2\sqrt{11} + 3\sqrt{11} + \sqrt{11}$$
$$= 6\sqrt{11}$$

($2\sqrt{11} + 3\sqrt{11} + \sqrt{11}$ could be thought of as
$2\sqrt{11} + 3\sqrt{11} + 1\sqrt{11}$ if that helps.)

4848. $\sqrt{144}$ means the principal square root of 144.
$\sqrt{144}$ is equal to 12.

4860. Simplify by rationalizing the denominator $\quad \dfrac{x + y}{\sqrt{6xy}}$

Multiplying top and bottom by $\sqrt{6xy}$ $\quad\quad = \dfrac{(x + y)\sqrt{6xy}}{\sqrt{6xy}\sqrt{6xy}}$

$$= \frac{(x + y)\sqrt{6xy}}{6xy} \quad \text{or} \quad \frac{x\sqrt{6xy} + y\sqrt{6xy}}{6xy} \quad \text{(either one is okay)}$$

The Complete Solutions and Answers

4900.

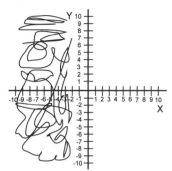

If the abscissa of a point is negative, then it could be any of the following: (−3, 7), (−2, 12), (−14, 30) . . . all of which are in Q II, or it could be (−5, −8), (−2, −4), (−π, −7) . . . all of which are in QIII.

4909. Solve by substitution $\begin{cases} 2x + 3y = 1 \\ y = 3x + 26 \end{cases}$

Substituting the value of y (which is 3x + 26) into the first equation:

$$2x + 3(3x + 26) = 1$$
$$2x + 9x + 78 = 1 \qquad \text{distributive law}$$
$$11x + 78 = 1 \qquad \text{combining}$$
$$11x = -77 \qquad \text{subtracting 78 from both sides}$$
$$x = -7$$

Substituting x = −7 into the second equation:
$$y = 3(-7) + 26$$
$$y = -21 + 26$$
$$y = 5$$

The complete solution is x = −7 and y = 5.

4911. $6x + 8y = 2(3x + 4y)$

You look for the largest thing that will divide evenly into 6x and 8y.
It is 2.
Then you write 2(   ).
Then you imagine using the distributive law and ask yourself

2 times ? would equal 6x.   2(3x +   ).

Then you ask yourself

2 times ? would equal 8y.   2(3x + 4y)

4912. $\sqrt{x + 14} = 4$ First step is to isolate the radical. That's already done. The second step is to square each side of the equation.
x + 14 = 16. So x = 2.
Checking the answer in the original equation: $\sqrt{2 + 14} \overset{?}{=} 4$. Yes.

The Complete Solutions and Answers

4913. Solve $6x^2 - x = 15$

Transpose to set it all equal to zero. $\qquad 6x^2 - x - 15 = 0$

Factor. We want two numbers that
multiply to $-90x^2$ and add to $-x$.

That would be $9x$ and $-10x$. $\qquad 6x^2 + 9x - 10x - 15 = 0$

Factor by grouping $\qquad\qquad\quad 3x(2x + 3) - 5(2x + 3) = 0$

$\qquad\qquad\qquad\qquad\qquad\qquad\qquad (2x + 3)(3x - 5) = 0$

Set each factor equal to zero $\qquad 2x + 3 = 0 \quad$ OR $\quad 3x - 5 = 0$

$\qquad\qquad\qquad\qquad\qquad\qquad\quad x = -3/2 \quad$ OR $\quad x = 5/3$

4940. Solve $\sqrt{x + 12} = -4$

First step is to isolate the radical. This has already been done.

Second step is to square both sides. $\qquad x + 12 = 16$

$\qquad\qquad\qquad\qquad\qquad\qquad\qquad\qquad\qquad x = 4$

The last step is to check the answer in the original equation.

$$\sqrt{4 + 12} \;\overset{?}{=}\; -4$$
$$\sqrt{16} \;\overset{?}{=}\; -4$$

No. $\sqrt{16}$ is equal to 4, not -4. There is no value of x that makes the original equation true.

By the way, if you had just looked at the original equation, you might have noticed that we have a square root equal to a negative number. In one step, you could announce that there is no solution.

4965. Your net worth was $-\$300$ in January and after your paycheck it became \$700. You went from -300 to 700.

Standard rule: If you went from x to y, your change is y – x.

Going from -300 to 700 is a change of $700 - (-300)$, which is \$1,000.

4977. To find the number to add to $x^2 + 12x$ to make it into a perfect square takes two steps. First, take half of the coefficient of the x-term. Half of $+12$ is $+6$. Square the $+6$. $\quad x^2 + 12x + 36$ is a perfect square.

It factors into $(x + 6)^2$.

Second example: If you wanted to make $x^2 - 10x$ into a perfect square, you take half of -10, which is -5 and square it: $x^2 - 10x + 25$. And that factors into $(x - 5)^2$.

196

The Complete Solutions and Answers

5000. It is not correct to write {3} + {22}. A plus sign can only go between two numbers. {3} is a set, not a number. It is the set that contains the number 3.

{elephant} is not an elephant. It is a set that contains the word *elephant*.

You could make {3} + {22} correct in one of two ways:

(1)   3 + 22   --------which is equal to 25 or

(2)   {3} ∪ {22} --------which is equal to {3, 22}.

5001. Solve $x^2 - 36 = 0$

It is already equal to zero.

Factor as a difference of squares $(x + 6)(x - 6) = 0$

Set each factor equal to zero $x + 6 = 0$ OR $x - 6 = 0$

                                       $x = -6$ OR $x = 6$.

This could also be written as $x = \pm 6$.

5004. Darlene liked to draw faces, but she was slow. Joe worked at a rate of 6 faces per minutes more than Darlene. In 4 minutes he drew as many faces as Darlene did in 12 minutes. How fast could Darlene draw faces?

① Using the Let r = . . . approach

Let r = the number of faces/minutes that Darlene could draw

Then r + 6 = the rate at which Joe could draw faces

Then 12r = the number of faces Darlene could draw in 12 minutes

Then 4(r + 6) = the number of faces Joe could draw in 4 minutes

Since Joe could draw as many in 4 minutes as Darlene could in 12 minutes, we have the equation

$$4(r + 6) = 12r$$
$$4r + 24 = 12r$$
$$24 = 8r$$
$$3 = r$$

Darlene could draw 3 faces per minute.

5009. Factor $2x^2 - 112 - 2x$

First arrange the terms $2x^2 - 2x - 112$

A common factor $2(x^2 - x - 56)$

Two numbers that multiply to −56
    and add to −1. $2(x - 8)(x + 7)$

The Complete Solutions and Answers

5010. $\sqrt{41 - x} = 6$

The first step is to isolate the radical on one side of the equation. That has been already done.

Second step is to square both sides. $\qquad$ $41 - x = 36$

$\qquad$ Add x to both sides $\qquad$ $41 = 36 + x$

$\qquad$ Subtract 36 from both sides $\qquad$ $5 = x$

The last step is to check the answer in the original equation.

$$\sqrt{41 - 5} \overset{?}{=} 6$$
$$\sqrt{36} \overset{?}{=} 6 \qquad \text{Yes. The answer checks.}$$

The final answer is $x = 5$.

5017. 6/11 expressed as a ratio is 6:11.

5020. Starting with $x^2 + 20x$, you take half of +20 and get +10. Square that and add it to the binomial: $x^2 + 20x + 100$.

$x^2 + 20x + 100$ factors into $(x + 10)^2$.

5022. $x + 1 \overline{)x^3 + 1}$

Fill in the missing terms and do the division.

$$
\begin{array}{r}
x^2 - x + 1 \\
x + 1 \overline{)x^3 + 0x^2 + 0x + 1} \\
\underline{x^3 + x^2} \\
-x^2 + 0x \\
\underline{-x^2 - x} \\
x + 1 \\
\underline{x + 1}
\end{array}
$$

Since $x + 1$ divides evenly into $x^3 + 1$, we can factor $x^3 + 1$ into

$$(x + 1)(x^2 - x + 1)$$

(In contrast, we can't factor $x^2 + 1$.)

5050. We will have no solution when $b^2 - 4ac$ is negative.

$\qquad$ Which of these quadratic equations have no solution?

A) $6x^2 - 4x + 1 = 0$ $\qquad$ $b^2 - 4ac = 16 - 24 < 0$ no solution

B) $2x^2 + 5x + 5 = 0$ $\qquad$ $b^2 - 4ac = 25 - 40 < 0$ no solution

C) $4x^2 + 10x + 31 = 0$ $\qquad$ $b^2 - 4ac = 100 - 496 < 0$ no solution

D) $5x^2 - 7x - 3 = 0$ $\qquad$ $b^2 - 4ac = 49 + 60 > 0$ solution exists

The Complete Solutions and Answers

5099. $\quad\quad\quad -4x + 1.5 > x$

$\quad\quad\quad\quad\quad 1.5 > 5x \quad\quad$ add 4x to both sides

$\quad\quad\quad\quad\quad 0.3 > x \quad\quad$ divide both sides by 5

5100. $10x^2 + 15xy^4 = 5x(2x + 3y^4)$

First you look for the biggest thing that will divide evenly into both $10x^2$ and into $15xy^4$. That is 5x.

Then, you write 5x (   ).

Then ask yourself 5x times what would equal $10x^2$?

$\quad\quad\quad 5x(2x + \quad)$

Then ask yourself 5x times what would equal $15xy^4$?

$\quad\quad\quad 5x(2x + 3y^4)$.

5101. Solve $10x^2 + 29x = -10$

Transpose everything to one side of the equation $\quad\quad 10x^2 + 29x + 10 = 0$

Factor the general trinomial.

Look for two numbers that multiply to $100x^2$

$\quad\quad\quad\quad$ and add to 29x $\quad\quad\quad\quad\quad\quad 10x^2 + 25x + 4x + 10 = 0$

Factor by grouping $\quad\quad\quad\quad\quad\quad\quad\quad 5x(2x + 5) + 2(2x + 5) = 0$

$\quad\quad\quad\quad\quad\quad\quad\quad\quad\quad\quad\quad\quad\quad\quad (2x + 5)(5x + 2) = 0$

Set each factor equal to zero $\quad\quad\quad\quad 2x + 5 = 0 \quad OR \quad 5x + 2 = 0$

$\quad\quad\quad\quad\quad\quad\quad\quad\quad\quad\quad\quad\quad x = -5/2 \quad OR \quad x = -2/5$

5104. Solve $\quad \begin{cases} 3x + y = 26 \\ 7x - 2y = 39 \end{cases}$

The y variable will be easier to eliminate than the x variable.

Multiply the top equation by 2 $\quad\quad 6x + 2y = 52$

Copy the second equation $\quad\quad\quad\quad 7x - 2y = 39$

Add the two equations $\quad\quad\quad\quad\quad\quad 13x = 91$

Divide both sides by 13 $\quad\quad\quad\quad\quad\quad x = 7$

Substitute x = 7 into the first equation $\quad\quad\quad\quad 3(7) + y = 26$

$\quad\quad\quad\quad\quad\quad\quad\quad\quad\quad\quad\quad\quad\quad 21 + y = 26$

$\quad\quad\quad\quad\quad\quad\quad\quad\quad\quad\quad\quad\quad\quad\quad y = 5$

The solution is x = 7 and y = 5.

The Complete Solutions and Answers

5107. Joe likes jelly beans where 9% of them are green. That makes him happiest. He has one jar that has 4% green jelly beans and another jar that has 16%. How much of each jar should he combine to make 24 kilograms where 9% of them are green?

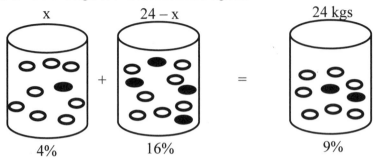

① Using the Let x = . . . approach

Let x = the number of kilograms of the 4% jar he'll use.

Then 24 – x = the number of kilograms of the 16% jar he'll use.

Then 0.04x = the number of green jelly beans contributed by the 4% jar.

Then 0.16(24 – x) = the number of green jelly beans contributed by the 16% jar.

Joe wants 0.09(24) kilograms of green jelly beans.

The kilograms of greenies from the 4% jar plus the kilograms of greenies from the 16% jar have to equal to kilograms of greenies in the final mixture.

$$0.04x + 0.16(24 - x) = 0.09(24)$$
$$0.04x + 3.84 - 0.16x = 2.16$$

Let's multiply through by 100 to get rid of all those decimals.

$$4x + 384 - 16x = 216$$
$$-12x + 384 = 216$$
$$384 - 216 = 12x$$
$$168 = 12x$$
$$14 = x$$

Joe will use 14 kilograms from the 4% jar and 10 kilograms (24 – x) from the 16% jar.

② Using the Six Pretty boxes approach

	kilograms of greenies	%	kilograms from each of the jars
the 4% jar	0.04x	0.04	x
the 16% jar	0.16(24 – x)	0.16	24 – x

The Complete Solutions and Answers

5111. $\{\heartsuit, \diamondsuit, \clubsuit\} \cup \{\heartsuit, \diamondsuit, \spadesuit\} = \{\heartsuit, \diamondsuit, \clubsuit, \spadesuit\}$

It would be a mistake to repeat some of the members more than once. It is not considered good "spelling" to write $\{\heartsuit, \diamondsuit, \clubsuit, \heartsuit, \diamondsuit, \spadesuit\}$. We made that rule ("No repetitions in the enumeration") to make it easier to count the number of members of a set.

5114. Solve $6x^2 - 54 = 0$

     You might notice that you could simplify the equation by dividing through by 6. You would get $x^2 - 9 = 0$.

     Let's suppose you didn't see that simplification.

     Everything is on one side, so we can factor.

     The kind of factoring, which you always look for first, is a common factor. $\qquad 6(x^2 - 9) = 0$

Difference of squares $\quad 6(x + 3)(x - 3) = 0$

We set each factor equal to zero

$$6 = 0 \quad \text{OR} \quad x + 3 = 0 \quad \text{OR} \quad x - 3 = 0$$

Since, for no value of x will 6 ever equal 0, we can discard the $6 = 0$.

$$x = -3 \quad \text{OR} \quad x = 3$$

This could also be written as $x = \pm 3$.

5117. $\dfrac{4x^2 - 1}{3x + 4} \div \dfrac{2x^2 + 9x - 5}{3x^2 + 19x + 20}$

You turn every division problem into a multiplication problem.

Back in arithmetic you turned $\dfrac{3}{4} \div \dfrac{2}{3}$ into $\dfrac{3}{4} \times \dfrac{3}{2}$

     In algebra you do the same thing. The fraction on the **right** of the division sign is the **right** one to turn upside down.

$$\frac{4x^2 - 1}{3x + 4} \div \frac{2x^2 + 9x - 5}{3x^2 + 19x + 20} = \frac{4x^2 - 1}{3x + 4} \times \frac{3x^2 + 19x + 20}{2x^2 + 9x - 5}$$

Top times top; bottom times bottom $\quad = \dfrac{(4x^2 - 1)(3x^2 + 19x + 20)}{(3x + 4)(2x^2 + 9x - 5)}$

Factor top, factor bottom $\quad = \dfrac{(2x + 1)(2x - 1)(3x + 4)(x + 5)}{(3x + 4)(2x - 1)(x + 5)}$

Cancel like factors $\quad = \dfrac{2x + 1}{1} = 2x + 1$

The Complete Solutions and Answers

5201. $12wx^3 - 16w^2x^5 = 4wx^3(3 - 4wx^2)$.

The easiest way to check this factoring is to multiply it out.

$4wx^3(3 - 4wx^2) = 12wx^3 - 16w^2x^5$

5203. The mean average for 4, 5, 6, 8, 8 is found by adding the numbers and dividing by 5.

$4 + 5 + 6 + 8 + 8$ equals 31. $31 \div 5 = 31/5$ or $6\frac{1}{5}$ or 6.2.

The median average is the one in the middle (after you have lined the numbers up in order). The median average is 6.

The mode average is the most common number in the list. Mode = 8.

5215. $8 + 4/2 = 8 + 2 = 10$ You do division before addition.

5222. The mean average of 6, 7, 11 is found by adding the three numbers and dividing by 3. $6 + 7 + 11 = 24.$ $24/3 = 8.$
The mean average is 8.

5225. 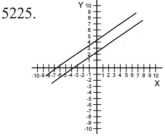 The equations are inconsistent. Since the lines are parallel, they will never meet. Because they don't meet, the two equations do not have a common solution. No pair of numbers will satisfy both equations at the same time.

Here is a pair of inconsistent equations: $\begin{cases} x + y = 2 \\ x + y = 3 \end{cases}$

Any pair of numbers that made the first equation true, could not make the second equation true. (Translation: If two numbers add to 2, they couldn't also add to 3.)

5231. If n is odd, then the next consecutive odd number after n is $n + 2$.
For example, the next consecutive odd number after 17 is 19.
If n is odd, then $n + 2$ will be odd.

The Complete Solutions and Answers

5234. Graph $y = 4x - 2$

If x = 0, then y = –2. plot (0, –2)

If x = 1, then y = 2. plot (1, 2)

If x = 2, then y = 6. plot (2, 6)

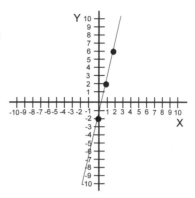

5236. $6x + 395x^2 - 17$ is not a quadratic equation, because it is not an equation. Equations have equals signs.

5240. $\dfrac{(w + 40)^8}{(w - 40)^2} \div \dfrac{(w + 40)^2}{w - 40}$

Invert (that means "turn upside down") and multiply

$$\frac{(w + 40)^8}{(w - 40)^2} \div \frac{(w + 40)^2}{w - 40} = \frac{(w + 40)^8(w - 40)}{(w - 40)^2(w + 40)^2}$$

Do you remember the rule $x^m \div x^n = x^{m-n}$

or, if you prefer, $\dfrac{x^m}{x^n} = x^{m-n}$?

We can use that here. The final answer is either $(w + 40)^6(w - 40)^{-1}$

$$\text{or} \quad \frac{(w + 40)^6}{w - 40}$$

Please do not go **cancel crazy** and cancel the 40s.

Please do not go **cancel crazy** and cancel the w's.

(Small English lesson: Plural of 40 is 40s. Plural of w is w's. English is harder than math.)

5252. If $x^2 = 36$, then $x = \pm\sqrt{36}$ which is ±6.

If you wrote just $x = \sqrt{36}$, that would mean that you lost the x = –6 part of the solution.

5266. By the symmetric law of equality, $4x^3 = 55$ becomes $55 = 4x^3$.

5300. Joe went out for a walk in the woods. When he was in the woods, he could spot bunnies on pogo sticks at the rate of 4 per minute.

When Joe got to the street, he saw bunnies painting lines on the street. He spent 30 fewer minutes on the street than in the woods. Bunnies painting lines were easier to spot. He saw them at the rate of 6 per minute.

He spotted the same number of each kind of bunny. How long was he in the woods spotting hopping bunnies?

❶ Using the Let x = . . . approach:

Let x = the minutes Joe was in the woods spotting bunnies on pogo sticks. (We almost always start by letting the variable equal the thing we are trying to find out.)

Then x – 30 = the number of minutes Joe was on the street spotting bunnies painting lines, since he was on the street 30 fewer minutes than in the woods.

Then 4x = the number of hopping bunnies, since he spent x minutes spotting hopping bunnies at the rate of 4/minute.

Then 6(x – 30) = the number of painting bunnies, since he spent x – 30 minutes spotting painting bunnies at the rate of 6/minute.

Since we are told that he saw the same number of each kind of bunny, we have the equation:

$$4x = 6(x - 30)$$
$$4x = 6x - 180 \qquad \text{distributive law}$$
$$-2x = -180 \qquad \text{subtract 6x from both sides}$$
$$x = 90 \qquad \text{divide both sides by } -2$$

Joe spent 90 minutes in the woods spotting bunnies on pogo sticks.

❷ Using the Six Pretty boxes approach:

	number of bunnies spotted	rate they are spotted	time spent
in the woods	4x	4/minute	x
on the street	6(x – 30)	6/minute	x – 30

5302. $6x^4y^4z^4 + 9xy^7z^3 = 3xy^4z^3(2x^3z + 3y^3)$

First, you look for the biggest thing that will divide evenly into $6x^4y^4z^4$ and $9xy^7z^3$. 3 is the largest number that will divide evenly into 6 and 9.

x is the largest power of x that will divide evenly into both x^4 and x.

y^4 is the largest power of y that will divide evenly into both y^4 and y^7.

z^3 is the largest power of z that will divide evenly into both z^4 and z^3.

Then write $3xy^4z^3($).

$3xy^4z^3$ times what equals $6x^4y^4z^4$? Write $3xy^4z^3(2x^3z +$).

Similarly, $3xy^4z^3$ times what equals $9xy^7z^3$? Write $3xy^4z^3(2x^3z + 3y^3)$.

The Complete Solutions and Answers

5304. Darlene's uncle had a square piece of land in Oklahoma. He bought more acreage that enlarged his original square into a rectangle. One side was now 1 mile larger than the original square. The other side was 3 miles larger than the original square. He now had 120 square miles of land. What were the dimensions of the original square?

Let x = the lengths of the sides of the original square.

Then $x + 1$ and $x + 3$ are the lengths of the enlarged property.

The area of the enlarged property is length × width, which in this case is $(x + 1)(x + 3)$.

The area of the enlarged property is 120 square miles.

$$(x + 1)(x + 3) = 120$$
$$x^2 + 3x + x + 3 = 120$$
$$x^2 + 4x + 3 = 120$$
$$x^2 + 4x - 117 = 0$$
$$(x + 13)(x - 9) = 0$$
$$x + 13 = 0 \quad \text{OR} \quad x - 9 = 0$$
$$x = -13 \quad \text{OR} \quad x = 9$$

$x = -13$ miles doesn't make sense in the measurement of land.
The final answer is: The original square was 9 miles by 9 miles.

5311. Suppose you are told that $\sqrt{x} = y$ (where x and y are real numbers). Since we are taking the square root of x, x can't be negative.
Since $\sqrt{x}$ means the principal square root of x, the answer (which is y) can't be negative.

For example, $\sqrt{-64}$ wouldn't make sense.

For example, $\sqrt{x} = -7$ wouldn't make sense.

5450. $24xy^2z^3 + 36xy^4z^2 + 48x^5y^2z^2 = 12xy^2z^2(2z + 3y^2 + 4x^4)$

One common mistake is not to find the *biggest* thing that will divide into each term. If, for example, you only used $6xy^2z^2$ instead of $12xy^2z^2$, your factoring would have been $6xy^2z^2(4z + 6y^2 + 8x^4)$. Notice that $(4z + 6y^2 + 8x^4)$ could still have another 2 factored out of it.

5454. Subtracting 82x from both sides, we get $- 71 < 1000$. This is always true. Hence, any value of x will make the original inequality true.

The Complete Solutions and Answers

5525. Some number times –3987 equals a positive answer. That number must be negative.

It couldn't be zero, since (0)(–3987) = 0.

If couldn't be positive, since any positive number times –3987 equals a negative answer.

5566. Since the table has a diameter of 56" and since the radius of a circle is one-half of the diameter,
$$56 \div 2 = \frac{56}{1} \div \frac{2}{1} = \frac{56}{1} \times \frac{1}{2} = \frac{56}{2} = 28".$$

5570. The invention of the tuning fork (by trumpeter John Shore) is five times as old as Catherine Marshall's book, *A Man Called Peter*.

Thirty (30) years ago the invention of the tuning fork was nine times as old as *A Man Called Peter*.

How many years ago did Catherine Marshall write *A Man Called Peter*?

Let t = how many years ago Catherine Marshall wrote *A Man Called Peter*.

Then 5t = how many years ago the tuning fork was invented.

Then t – 30 = how old *A Man Called Peter* was 30 years ago.

Then 5t – 30 = how old the tuning fork was 30 years ago.

Finally, since the tuning fork 30 years ago was nine times as old as *A Man Called Peter* was 30 years ago, we have the equation

5t – 30 = 9(t – 30)	
5t – 30 = 9t – 270	distributive property
5t + 240 = 9t	add 270 to both sides
240 = 4t	subtract 5t from both sides
60 = t	divide both sides by 4

Catherine Marshall wrote *A Man Called Peter* 60 years ago.

5580. Filling in each blank with either ∈ or ∉:

5 ∈ {–2, –1, 0, 1, 2, . . . , 40, 41, 42}

7 ∈ the set of integers

△ ∉ {⊛, ◎, ⊨, 𝕀}

5585. x > z if and only if z < x.

"If and only if" is sometimes abbreviated as iff.

The word *iff* is listed in my dictionary.

The Complete Solutions and Answers

5588. Solve by substitution $\begin{cases} 2x + 6y = -4 \\ 7x + 16y = 1 \end{cases}$

We need to pick one of the two equations and solve it for one of the variables. (If you chose y in the second equation, you would have a real mess: $7x + 16y = 1 \rightarrow 16y = -7x + 1 \rightarrow y = \frac{-7x + 1}{16}$)

Instead, I will solve the first equation for x: $2x + 6y = -4$
$$2x = -6y - 4$$
$$x = -3y - 2 \quad \bigstar$$

Substitute this value of x, which is $-3y - 2$, into the second equation:
$$7(-3y - 2) + 16y = 1$$
$$-21y - 14 + 16y = 1$$
$$-5y - 14 = 1$$
$$-5y = 15$$
$$y = -3$$

Substitute $y = -3$ into any equation containing both variables. The easiest is $x = -3y - 2$. (I marked that equation with a $\bigstar$.)
$$x = -3(-3) - 2$$
$$x = 7$$
The final answer is $x = 7$ and $y = -3$.

5590. { y | y = 2n where n is a whole number} = {0, 2, 4, 6, 8 . . . }.
The whole numbers are {0, 1, 2, 3, 4, 5, . . .}.
If y is equal to twice some whole number, then y would have to be one of: 0, 2, 4, 6, etc.

5592. $18aby - 25bxy = by(18a - 25x)$
There wasn't much that could be factored out.

5595. $\sqrt{x} = x$ is true when x is equal to either zero or one. You could have solved that by "just looking," or you could go through all the steps of solving the radical equation.
Namely, first, square both sides. $x = x^2$. Next, solve by factoring. Put everything on the right side. $0 = x^2 - x$. Factor. $0 = x(x - 1)$
Set each factor equal to zero. $x = 0$ OR $x - 1 = 0$.
So either $x = 0$ OR $x = 1$.

The Complete Solutions and Answers

5597. Solve $10xw - 45x + 12w = 54$

Set everything equal to zero	$10xw - 45x + 12w - 54 = 0$
Since there are four terms, we	$5x(2w - 9) + 6(2w - 9) = 0$
factor by grouping	$(2w - 9)(5x + 6) = 0$
Set each factor equal to zero	$2w - 9 = 0$ OR $5x + 6 = 0$
	$w = 9/2$ OR $x = -6/5$

For fun, let's check one of the answers.

I'll put $w = 9/2$ into the original equation

$$10x(9/2) - 45x + 12(9/2) \overset{?}{=} 54$$
$$45x - 45x + 54 \overset{?}{=} 54$$
$$54 = 54$$

Yes. It checks.

5598. The set of integers is $\{ \ldots -3, -2, -1, 0, 1, 2, \ldots \}$.

English lesson: Those three periods are called an ellipsis. An ellipsis always has three periods. An ellipsis indicates you have left something out.

I wrote $\{ \ldots -3, -2, -1, 0, 1, 2, \ldots \}$ since I couldn't possibly write out all the integers, even if I spent all afternoon.

Suppose you want to shorten the quote: "I freely, happily, heartily, accept the award." You could write, "I freely . . . accept the award."

Note the spaces on either side of the ellipsis.

On the other hand, suppose you want to shorten the quote: "I got the award. John is happy. Mary left town."

If I want to eliminate the second sentence, it would look like: "I got the award. . . . Mary left town."

I did *not* use four periods in the ellipsis. The first period is right next to the *d*, and it is the period in the sentence. The next three periods are the ellipsis. Notice that I have the official space between the ellipsis and the period of the previous sentence.

Not good: I got the award....

Not good: I got the award . . . .

Not good: I got the award. . . . . . .

Lots of people don't know how to use ellipses. (pronounced ee-LIP-sees)

The Complete Solutions and Answers

5600. Twenty-five years ago, Pat was twice as old as Chris. Today, Pat is five years older than Chris. What is Pat's present age?

You almost always start a word problem by letting the variable equal the thing you are trying to find out.

Let x = Pat's present age.

> *There is no way you can jump from the English directly to the equation.*

Then x – 5 = Chris's present age. (Chris is 5 years younger than Pat.)

Then x – 25 = Pat's age 25 years ago.

Then (x – 5) – 25 = Chris's age 25 years ago = x – 30

We are told than Pat's age 25 years ago is twice Chris's age 25 years ago.

So   x – 25   = 2 (x – 30)

$$x - 25 = 2(x - 30)$$

x – 25 = 2x – 60	distributive property
–25 = x – 60	subtract x from both sides
35 = x	add 60 to both sides

Pat's present age is 35 years.

5606. 64 – (–8) = 64 + (+8) = 72   or +72.

5607. 3x – 5 = 7x – 11

– 5 = 4x – 11	Subtracting 3x from both sides.
6 = 4x	Adding 11 to both sides.
$\frac{6}{4}$ = x	Dividing both sides by 4
$\frac{3}{2}$ = x	Simplifying.

$x = 1\frac{1}{2}$ or x = 1.5 are also okay.

5608. Subtracting 6x from both sides of 6x – 11 > 6x + 3 we obtain –11 > 3. This is never true. Hence, no values of x will make the original inequality true.

The Complete Solutions and Answers

5609. We started with a square where each side was s centimeters long. We increased one side by 3 centimeters and decreased the other side by 4 centimeters. The resulting rectangle had an area of 60 square centimeters. What is the length of a side of the original square?

For geometry word problems, it often helps to draw a picture.
The area of the rectangle is 60 square centimeters.
Therefore, $(s - 4)(s + 3) = 60$
Don't set $s - 4$ equal to zero. You can only do that after you have an equation with two (or more) factors which multiply to zero.

Multiplying out the left side	$s^2 - s - 12 = 60$
Putting everything on one side	$s^2 - s - 72 = 0$
Now we factor	$(s + 8)(s - 9) = 0$
Set each factor equal to zero	$s + 8 = 0$ OR $s - 9 = 0$
	$s = -8$ OR $s = 9$

The final answer is $s = 9$. The length of the side of the square is equal to 9 centimeters.

It doesn't make much sense to talk about a square whose sides are –8 centimeters.

5611. Solve $3x + 4x^2 = -1$
First, place it in general form for quadratic equations. $4x^2 + 3x + 1 = 0$
We note that $a = 4$, $b = 3$, and $c = 1$.

Using the quadratic formula:
$$x = \frac{-3 \pm \sqrt{9 - 4(4)(1)}}{8}$$

$$x = \frac{-3 \pm \sqrt{-7}}{8}$$

We have a negative number under the square root.
There is no solution. No value of x will make $3x + 4x^2 = -1$ true.

The Complete Solutions and Answers

5692. When x is equal to –25, then $\sqrt{-x} = 5$ is true.
Explanation: If x = –25, then –x is equal to 25.

5700. The coefficient of $w^5x^2y^8$ is 1. (Consider $w^5x^2y^8$ as $1w^5x^2y^8$.)

5707. The mode average of 3, 4, 5, 5, 5, 6, 6, 7, 7, 7 ,7, 398 the found by naming the most common number in the list. The number 7 appears four times on the list. The mode average is 7.

5709. In graphing $x = y^2 - 3$, the easiest thing to do is assign values to y and then find the corresponding x-values.

If y = 0, then x = –3.	We plot the point (–3, 0).
If y = 1, then x = –2.	We plot the point (–2, 1).
If y = –1, then x = –2.	We plot the point (–2, –1).

We suddenly notice that a positive value of y will give the same x as the negative value of y. We can shorten things up:

If y = ±2, then x = 1.	We plot both (1, 2) and (1, –2).
If y = ±3, then x = 6.	We plot both (6, 3) and (6, –3).

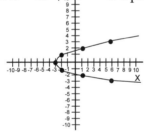

5712. $\dfrac{y^6}{y^2} = y^4$ by the rule $x^m \div x^n = x^{m-n}$

In this particular problem: $\dfrac{yyyyyy}{yy} = yyyy$

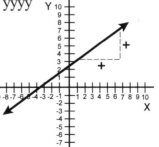

5740. If we draw in a little triangle for the rise and run, we see that both the rise and the run are positive.

Therefore rise/run will be positive.

The slope is positive.

The Complete Solutions and Answers

5790. Solve $30x^3 + 5x = -31x^2$

Put everything on one side of the equation $\qquad 30x^3 + 31x^2 + 5x = 0$

Factor. You always look for a common factor first $\quad x(30x^2 + 31x + 5) = 0$

Two numbers that multiply to $150x^2$ and
add to $31x$ are $25x$ and $6x$. $\qquad x(30x^2 + 25x + 6x + 5) = 0$

Factor by grouping $\qquad\qquad x(5x(6x + 5) + (6x + 5)) = 0$

$$x(6x + 5)(5x + 1) = 0$$

Set each of the factors equal to zero $\quad x = 0 \ \ \text{OR} \ \ 6x + 5 = 0 \ \ \text{OR} \ 5x + 1 = 0$

$$x = 0 \ \ \text{OR} \ \ x = -5/6 \ \ \ \text{OR} \ x = -1/5$$

5792. Ten apples and three bananas cost 155¢.

It is an even trade if you exchange one apple for two bananas and 4¢.

Using two equations and two unknowns and solving by substitution determine how much one apple costs.

Let x = the cost of one apple.

Let y = the cost of one banana.

$$\begin{cases} 10x + 3y = 155 \\ \ \ x = 2y + 4 \end{cases}$$

x¢   y¢

Substituting the value of x, which is $2y + 4$, into the first equation:

$10(2y + 4) + 3y = 155$

$\quad 20y + 40 + 3y = 155 \qquad$ distributive property

$\qquad\quad 23y + 40 = 155 \qquad$ combine terms

$\qquad\qquad\quad 23y = 115 \qquad$ subtract 40 from both sides

$\qquad\qquad\quad\ \ y = 5 \qquad\quad$ divide both sides by 23

The question asks for the cost of an apple, which is the value of x.

We substitute $y = 5$ into the second equation: $\qquad x = 2(5) + 4$

An apple costs 14¢. $\qquad\qquad\qquad\qquad\qquad\qquad x = 14$

5795. $44 \div 13$ as a ratio is 44:13.

5799. The square of 7 is positive. 48^2 is positive.

$(-9)^2$ is positive. π^2 is positive. $(-\pi)^2$ is positive (and equals π^2).
$(\sqrt{783})^2$ is positive (and equals 783).

But there is one real number, which when squared is not positive. That number is 0.

The Complete Solutions and Answers

5800. Solve $x^3 - 4x^2 + 3x = 12$

Transpose everything to one side $\qquad x^3 - 4x^2 + 3x - 12 = 0$

Factor by grouping $\qquad\qquad\qquad x^2(x - 4) + 3(x - 4) = 0$

$\qquad\qquad\qquad\qquad\qquad\qquad (x - 4)(x^2 + 3) = 0$

Set each factor equal to zero $\qquad x - 4 = 0 \quad OR \quad x^2 + 3 = 0$

$\qquad\qquad\qquad\qquad\qquad\qquad x = 4$ is the only solution.

$x^2 + 3$ could never equal zero. Why? The smallest that x^2 could ever be is zero. x^2 (when x is any real number) can never be negative.
If the smallest that x^2 can be is zero, then the smallest that $x^2 + 3$ can ever be is 3. Thus $x^2 + 3$ can never equal zero.

5812. Solve $0 = 3x^2 + 9x - 5$.

Divide through by 3 to make the
coefficient of the x^2 term equal to one. $\qquad 0 = x^2 + 3x - \dfrac{5}{3}$

Transpose the number to the left side and
complete the square. $\qquad\qquad \dfrac{5}{3} + \dfrac{9}{4} = x^2 + 3x + \dfrac{9}{4}$
(Half of 3 is 3/2. $(3/2)^2 = 9/4$)

Arithmetic on the left side and
factor the right side. $\qquad\qquad\qquad \dfrac{47}{12} = (x + \dfrac{3}{2})^2$

Take the square root of each side and
add a $\pm$.

$\qquad\qquad\qquad\qquad\qquad \pm\sqrt{\dfrac{47}{12}} = x + \dfrac{3}{2}$

Transpose the $\dfrac{3}{2}$ $\qquad\qquad\qquad \dfrac{-3}{2} \pm \sqrt{\dfrac{47}{12}} = x$

If we want to rationalize the denominator of $\sqrt{\dfrac{47}{12}}$ multiplying top and bottom by $\sqrt{3}$ will be enough. (We don't have to multiply by $\sqrt{12}$.)

$$\dfrac{\sqrt{47}}{\sqrt{12}}\dfrac{\sqrt{3}}{\sqrt{3}} = \dfrac{\sqrt{47}\sqrt{3}}{6}$$

5816. $6y + 38 + 4y = 68$

$\qquad\qquad 10y + 38 = 68 \qquad$ Combining like terms.

$\qquad\qquad\quad 10y = 30 \qquad$ Subtracting 38 from both sides.

$\qquad\qquad\qquad y = 3 \qquad$ Dividing both sides by 10.

The Complete Solutions and Answers

6019. In a right triangle the shortest leg is 10 meters shorter than the other leg. The hypotenuse is 50 meters long. How long is the shorter leg?

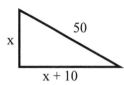

We almost always begin a word problem by letting the variable equal the thing we are trying to find out.

Let x = the length of the shorter leg.

Then x + 10 = the length of the longer leg.

By the Pythagorean theorem, $x^2 + (x + 10)^2 = 50^2$

$$x^2 + x^2 + 20x + 100 = 2500$$
$$2x^2 + 20x - 2400 = 0$$

Divide everything by 2 $x^2 + 10x - 1200 = 0$

Find two numbers that multiply to –1200 and add to 10.   +40 and –30 $(x + 40)(x - 30) = 0$

Set each factor equal to zero   x + 40 = 0   OR   x – 30 = 0

x = 30 meters

(x = – 40 meters doesn't make any sense for the length of a leg.)

6021. $\dfrac{5}{y - 12} + \dfrac{17 - y}{12 - y}$

The least common multiple is not (y – 12)(12 – y). That's too large. We can make the denominators alike by multiplying the second fraction on the top and bottom by –1.

$$\frac{5}{y - 12} + \frac{17 - y}{12 - y} = \frac{5}{y - 12} + \frac{(17 - y)(-1)}{(12 - y)(-1)}$$

$$= \frac{5 + (17 - y)(-1)}{y - 12}$$

$$= \frac{5 - 17 + y}{y - 12}$$

$$= \frac{y - 12}{y - 12} = 1$$

6025. {x | x = a/b where a and b are integers and b ≠ 0} is the set of **rational numbers**. All of these are rational numbers: 7/3, –5/8, 200, 4.3238, $\sqrt{144}$, and 0, because each of these can be written as an integer divided by a non-zero integer. 200 = 200/1, 4.3238 = 43238/10000, $\sqrt{144}$ = 12/1, and 0 = 0/83.

The Complete Solutions and Answers

6111. Stanthony's personal-sized pizza has a diameter that is 8 inches less than the Stanthony's pizza-for-two. The pizza-for-two is 80π square inches larger than the personal-sized pizza. What is the diameter of the personal-sized pizza?

The area of a circle is $A = \pi r^2$. To make the arithmetic a little easier, I'm going to let r = the *radius* of the smaller pizza.

Then the area of the smaller pizza is πr^2.

Then the radius of the larger pizza is r + 4. (If the diameter is 8" larger, then the radius is 4" larger.)

Then the area of the larger pizza is $\pi(r + 4)^2$.

The difference between the areas is 80π square inches.

$$\pi(r + 4)^2 - \pi r^2 = 80\pi$$

Dividing each term by π
$$(r + 4)^2 - r^2 = 80$$
$$r^2 + 8r + 16 - r^2 = 80$$
$$8r + 16 = 80$$
$$8r = 64$$
$$r = 8$$

The *diameter* of the personal-sized pizza is 16 inches.

6115. Will this quadratic equation have a solution?
$$9926492390262x^2 - 343590003027x - 98929939946369282862 = 0$$

First of all, b^2 will always be positive.

$-4ac$ in this case will be (−4)(positive number)(negative number) so $-4ac$ will be positive.

$b^2 - 4ac$ will be positive number + positive number.

$b^2 - 4ac$ will be positive.   There will be a solution.

6117. In order to find the slope of the line $66 = 3x - 5y$ we first need to put the equation in the y = mx + b form.

$$66 = 3x - 5y$$

Transpose the −5y and the 66. $5y = 3x - 66$

Divide both sides by 5. $y = (3/5)x - 66/5$

The slope is equal to 3/5.

The Complete Solutions and Answers

6121. $(+8)(-7) = -56$. The signs are different so the answer is negative.

$(-9)(-6) = +54$. Signs alike $\Rightarrow$ Answer positive.

$(10)(-10) = -100$.

6122. The Song of Deborah is four times as old as the first toll road ever build in England.

Three hundred seventy-one (371) years from now the Song of Deborah will be three times as old as the road.

How old (today) is the first toll road ever built in England?

Let x = the current age of the first toll road. (To begin a word problem, let the variable equal the thing you are trying to find out.)

Then 4x = the current age of the Song of Deborah.

Then x + 371 = the age of the road 371 years from now.

Then 4x + 371 = the age of the song 371 years from now.

Finally, since we know that the age of the song 371 years from now will be three times the age of the road 371 years from now, we have the equation:

$$4x + 371 = 3(x + 371)$$

age of song | is three times | age of road
371 years from | | 371 years from
now | | now

$$4x + 371 = 3x + 1113 \qquad \text{distributive law}$$
$$4x = 3x + 742 \qquad \text{subtract 371 from both sides}$$
$$x = 742 \qquad \text{subtract 3x from both sides}$$

The current age of the first toll road in England is 742 years.

6124. Five consecutive numbers that add to 980.

Let n = the first number.

Then n + 1 = the second consecutive number.

Then n + 2 = the third consecutive number.

Then n + 3 = the fourth consecutive number.

Then n + 4 = the fifth consecutive number.

Then since the sum of these five consecutive numbers equals 980, we have the equation:

$$n + (n+1) + (n+2) + (n+3) + (n+4) = 980$$
$$n + n + 1 + n + 2 + n + 3 + n + 4 = 980$$
$$5n + 10 = 980$$

subtracting 10 from both sides $\qquad 5n = 970$

dividing both sides by 5 $\qquad n = 194$

The question asks for all five consecutive numbers.

They are 194, 195, 196, 197, and 198.

The Complete Solutions and Answers

6127. Darlene and Joe are 600 feet from each other. They run toward each other. Joe runs 80 ft/minute and Darlene runs 120 ft/minute. How long before they meet?

Note that in some d = rt problems, one person is chasing another, and they both travel the same distance. In this d = rt problem, the people do *not* travel the same distance. Instead we know the total distance that both of them travel.

❶ Using the Let t = . . . approach:

Let t = the minutes that Darlene ran. (We start word problems by letting the variable equal the thing we are trying to find out.)

Then t = the minutes that Joe ran. (Joe ran the same length of time as Darlene.)

Then 120t = the distance that Darlene ran. (She ran at 120 ft/min for t minutes.)

Then 80t = the distance that Joe ran.

Finally, since we know that together they ran 600 feet, we have the equation: $120t + 80t = 600$

Adding $200t = 600$

Dividing both sides by 200 $t = 3$

They meet in 3 minutes.

❷ Using the Six Pretty Boxes approach:

	d	r	t ·
Darlene			t
Joe			

$\rightarrow$

	d	r	t
Darlene			t
Joe			t

$\leftarrow$

	d	r	t
Darlene		120	t
Joe		80	t

$\rightarrow$

	d	r	t
Darlene	120t	120	t
Joe	80t	80	t

6129. 0.03 can be written as $\frac{3}{100}$. The definition of a rational number is any number that can be expressed as an integer divided by a non-zero integer. Therefore, 0.03 is a rational number.

The Complete Solutions and Answers

6130. The mean average of 0, 0, 1, 1 is found by adding up the four numbers and dividing by four. The sum is 2. $2/4 = \frac{1}{2}$ (or 0.5).

6148. For every 5 cherry-flavored balls, he has 2 blueberry-flavored, 11 chocolate-flavored and 7 mint-flavored balls. He has a total of 625 gum balls in those four flavors.

$$5:2:11:7$$
$$5x:2x:11x:7x$$
$$5x + 2x + 11x + 7x = 625$$
$$25x = 625$$
$$x = 25$$

The question asks for how many of each flavor.
The cherry-flavored is represented by 5x. $5(25) = 125$
The blueberry-flavored is represented by 2x. $2(25) = 50$
Chocolate-flavored is 11x. $11(25) = 275$
Mint-flavored is 7x. $7(25) = 175$.

Note that if we add up these four answers $(125 + 50 + 275 + 175)$ we get 625. Our answer makes sense.

6149. This property $a(b + c) = ab + ac$ is called the distributive property.

6150. In graphing $x = y^2 + y$, the easiest approach is to name values for y and then find the corresponding values for x.

If $y = 0$, then $x = 0$.   We plot the point $(0, 0)$.
If $y = 1$, then $x = 2$.   We plot the point $(2, 1)$.
If $y = -1$, then $x = 0$.   We plot the point $(0, -1)$.
If $y = 2$, then $x = 6$.   We plot the point $(6, 2)$.
If $y = -2$, then $x = 2$.   We plot the point $(2, -2)$.
If $y = -3$, then $x = 6$.   We plot the point $(6, -3)$.

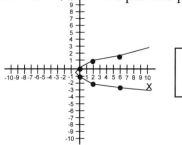

Note: The curve passes through the origin.

The Complete Solutions and Answers

6179. Joe wants to make 30 pounds of chili seasoning that contains 30% cayenne pepper. He has one sack of mild chili seasoning that is 10% cayenne and one sack of hot chili seasoning that is 40% cayenne.

How much of each sack should he use?

❶ Using the Let x = approach:

Let x = the number of pounds of mild seasoning he uses. (Since we want to find out two different things, we can let x equal either one of them.)

Then 30 – x = the number of pounds of hot seasoning he uses. (If he uses x pounds of the mild and 30 pounds altogether, then he has to use 30 – x of the hot.)

The first trick for doing mixture problems is to compute the amount of the "ingredient" in the sacks you are combining.

Then 0.1x = the pounds of cayenne in the mild seasoning that he uses. (10% = 0.1 He is using x pounds of which 10% is cayenne.)

Then 0.4(30 – x) = the pounds of cayenne contributed by the hot seasoning. (He is using 30 – x pounds of which 40% is cayenne.)

The second trick in mixture problems is to compute the amount of the "ingredient" in the final mixture that is desired. In this case, we want 30 pounds with 30% cayenne. So the amount of the ingredient in the final mixture is 0.3(30) which is 9 pounds of cayenne.

You will get a lot of practice with decimals and percents in these mixture problems. Note that to change a percent like 82.357% into a decimal, you move the decimal two places to the left and get 0.82357. The old saying: *When the percent has left, you move the decimal to the left.*

Finally, the equation is 0.1x + 0.4(30 – x) = 9 (since the amount of ingredient (cayenne) contributed by the mild is 0.1x and by the hot is 0.4(30 – x), and the total amount in the desired mixture is 9.

distributive property	$0.1x + 12 - 0.4x = 9$
combine 0.1x and –0.4x	$-0.3x + 12 = 9$
add 0.3x to both sides	$12 = 9 + 0.3x$
subtract 9 from both sides	$3 = 0.3x$
divide both sides by 0.3	$10 = x$

Joe uses 10 pounds of the mild seasoning and 20 pounds (which is 30 – x) of the hot seasoning. (The question asked how much of *each* sack.)

❷ When you fill in the Six Pretty Boxes . . .

	lbs. of cayenne	% of cayenne in the seasoning	lbs. of each seasoning used
mild seasoning	0.1x	10%	x
hot seasoning	0.4(30 – x)	40%	30 – x

The Complete Solutions and Answers

6181. $(-5)(+7)(-2) = (-35)(-2) = 70$ (or +70)

6187. $(99.392)(⅓)(\sqrt{311})(0)(-100)(0.33333333) = 0$. If zero is one of the factors in a product, the answer will always be zero.

6190. The median average of 0, 3, 4, 19, 9362 is found by lining up all the number in order and picking the middle one.
    There are already in order. The middle one is 4. Four is the median average of 0, 3, 4, 19, 9362.

6204. Suppose a pizza had a diameter of 7 feet and using $\frac{22}{7}$ for π, the circumference of this pizza would be $C = \pi d \approx \frac{22}{7} \times 7 = \frac{22}{7} \times \frac{7}{1} = \frac{22}{\cancel{7}} \times \frac{\cancel{7}}{1} = 22$ feet.

6207.   Two rats and 5 mice cost $11.
        Four rats and 3 mice cost $15.
How much does one rat cost? How much does one mouse cost?
    Let x = cost of a rat.
    Let y = cost of one mouse.
Then $\begin{cases} 2x + 5y = 11 \\ 4x + 3y = 15 \end{cases}$
Eliminating the x variable is easier than eliminating the y variable.
Multiplying the first equation by -2: $\begin{cases} -4x - 10y = -22 \\ 4x + 3y = 15 \end{cases}$

Adding the two equations: $-7y = -7$
Dividing both sides by -7 $y = 1$

Substituting $y = 1$ into the first equation: $2x + 5(1) = 11$
                                                $2x = 6$
                                                 $x = 3$

A rat costs $3 and a mouse costs $1.

6210. The union of the whole numbers and the natural numbers is $\{0, 1, 2, 3, 4, \ldots\} \cup \{1, 2, 3, 4, \ldots\}$ which is $\{0, 1, 2, 3, 4, \ldots\}$. The union of the whole numbers and the natural numbers is the whole numbers.

220

The Complete Solutions and Answers

6215. Is it true that $-14 < -100$? No. -100 is to the left of -14 on the number line. -100 is less than -14. If you owe $100 you are poorer than if you only owe $14.

6222. Its perimeter is $15 + 15 + 40 + 40 = 110$ miles.
The perimeter is the distance around the outside.
It is equal to two widths plus two lengths.

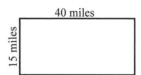

Its area is $15 \times 40 = 600$ square miles.
The area of a rectangle is the length times the width.

6234. *Every real number is either positive or negative or zero.* Some books call this the Law of Trichotomy. (tri-COT-eh-me) *tri* means three parts. —*tomy* means cutting. When they cut out your appendix, it is called an appendectomy.

6274. Find three consecutive even numbers that add to 2166.
    The first step in almost any word problem is to "Let n = . . ." the thing you are trying to find out.
    Let n = the first of the three consecutive even numbers.
    The second step in almost any word problem is to write "Then . . ." statements based on the "Let n = . . ." statement.
    Then $n + 2 =$ the second consecutive even number.
    Then $n + 4 =$ the third consecutive even number.
We are told that they add to 2166, so we can write the equation:
$$n + (n + 2) + (n + 4) = 2166$$
$$3n + 6 = 2166$$
subtracting 6 from both sides $\qquad 3n = 2160$
dividing both sides by 3 $\qquad n = 720$
    We are not done. The question asked that we find three consecutive numbers. $\qquad n = 720$ is the first one.
$$n + 2 = 722 \text{ is the second one.}$$
$$n + 4 = 724 \text{ is the third.}$$
    Checking our answer:
    ☞ Are they consecutive and even? Yes. 720, 722, and 724
    ☞ Do the add to 2166? Yes. $720 + 722 + 724$ add to 2166.

The Complete Solutions and Answers

6277. $(z^4)^8 = z^{32}$ by the rule $(x^m)^n = x^{mn}$
In this particular problem: $(z^4)^8 =$
$(zzzz)(zzzz)(zzzz)(zzzz)(zzzz)(zzzz)(zzzz)(zzzz) = z^{32}$

6288. If you multiply six negative numbers together, the answer will be positive.

For example: $(-2)(-5)(-3)(-100)(-\frac{1}{2})(-0.4)$

You work from
left to right ➔➔➔
when doing the
multiplications.

$= (+10)(-3)(-100)(-\frac{1}{2})(-0.4)$

$= (-30)(-100)(-\frac{1}{2})(-0.4)$

$= (+3000)(-\frac{1}{2})(-0.4)$

$= (-1500)(-0.4)$

$= +600$

6290. We know that π is irrational. That means that it cannot be expressed as a/b where a and b are integers and $b \neq 0$. Make an argument to show that 7π must be irrational.

We know that every real number must be either rational or irrational. If I can show that 7π is not rational, that will prove that it must be irrational.

If 7π were rational, then it would have to be some integers, a and b, such that $7\pi = \frac{a}{b}$.

Then we divide both sides by 7 and get $\pi = \frac{a}{7b}$.
That would make π a rational number. That's nonsense.
Therefore, our assumption that 7π is rational must be false.
So 7π must be irrational.

Here is an example of an argument by contradiction. *If you tell me that this stock is going to triple in value in this next week, why are you willing to sell it to me now?*

6300. $(-12)/(+3) = -4$ If the signs are different ⇨ Answer is negative
$(-54)/(-9) = +6$ If the signs are alike ⇨ Answer positive
$(36)/(-9) = -4$
$(10)/(-100) = -\frac{1}{10}$ (or -0.1)

The Complete Solutions and Answers

6302. In order to find the mode average, it often is easier first to line the numbers up from smallest to largest. If we place 6, 9, 6, 9, 342, 6 in numerical order, they become 6, 6, 6, 9, 9, 342.

Now it's easier to see that 6 is the most common number. The mode average of 6, 9, 6, 9, 342, 6 is 6.

6303. Joe and Darlene decided to drive a tractor. Joe could drive it at 4 mph. Darlene at 6 mph. Joe drove it first and then let Darlene drive it. Together, they drove the tractor 12 hours and covered 67 miles. How long did Joe drive it?

Let t = the number of hours Joe drove.

Then 12 – t = the number of hours Darlene drove.

Then 4t = the distance Joe drove. (He drove at 4 mph for t hours.)

Then 6(12 – t) = the distance Darlene drove. (She drove at 6 mph for 12 – t hours.

$$4t + 6(12 - t) = 67$$
$$4t + 72 - 6t = 67$$
$$-2t + 72 = 67$$
$$5 = 2t$$
$$\frac{5}{2} = t$$

Joe drove for $\frac{5}{2}$ hours, which is 2½ hours, or 2 hours and 30 minutes.

Using Six Pretty boxes:

	distance	rate	time
Joe	4t	4	t
Darlene	6(12 – t)	6	12 – t

6304. In a right triangle, the hypotenuse is equal to 15, and one leg is equal to 10. What is the length of the other leg? Simplify your answer (but do not approximate it).

By the Pythagorean theorem:
$$10^2 + x^2 = 15^2$$
$$100 + x^2 = 225$$
$$x^2 = 125$$
$$x = \sqrt{125}$$
$$x = \sqrt{25}\sqrt{5}$$
$$x = 5\sqrt{5}$$

We ignore
$x = -\sqrt{125}$
since we are dealing with lengths.

The Complete Solutions and Answers

6305. Three of Dorothenia's muffins and two of her pies weigh a total of 22 pounds. Seven of her muffins and one pie weigh 33 pounds. How much does one of her muffins weigh?

(Dorothenia is a witch, played by Mrs. Bright in a kindergarten play, in Chapter 22 of *Life of Fred: Calculus*. She made some nice things for Fred and his friends to eat.)

Let x = the weight of one of Dorothenia's muffins.

Let y = the weight of one of her pies.

Then
$$\begin{cases} 3x + 2y = 22 \\ 7x + y = 33 \end{cases}$$

It will be easier to eliminate the y variable than the x variable.

Multiplying the second equation by –2
$$\begin{cases} 3x + 2y = 22 \\ -14x - 2y = -66 \end{cases}$$

Adding the two equations together $\qquad -11x = -44$

Dividing both sides by –11 $\qquad x = 4$

One of Dorothenia's muffins weighs 4 pounds. (We were not asked to determine the weight of one of her pies.)

6308. For every 3 pizzas I eat, I gain 2 pounds. The ratio of pizzas to pounds to 3:2.

6311. $(10w^8)^6 = 10^6 w^{48}$ $\qquad\qquad (xy)^m = x^m y^m$

6315. Solve by substitution $\begin{cases} 3x + 2y = 19 \\ x = -5y - 11 \end{cases}$

The second equation is already solved for x. We take that value of x, which is –5y – 11, and substitute it into the first equation:

$3(-5y - 11) + 2y = 19$

We now have one equation with one unknown.

$-15y - 33 + 2y = 19$	distributive law
$-13y - 33 = 19$	combining
$-13y = 52$	adding 33 to both sides
$y = -4$	dividing both sides by –13

Substituting y = –4 into the second equation: $\quad x = -5(-4) - 11$
$$x = 9$$

The final answer is x = 9 and y = –4.

The Complete Solutions and Answers

6320. Draw a picture of a circle and then draw a radius. I like circles so I drew a bunch of them with their radii. (*Radii* is the plural of *radius*.) RAY-de-eye

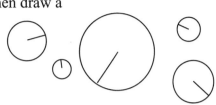

6323. A hiker went to collect 1000 wild flowers for his girl friend. She wanted 20% of them to be red. The lower trail had 15% red flowers and the upper trail had 35% red flowers. (He was color blind.) How many flowers should he pick from the lower trail?

Method ① (Using "Let x = . . . ")

Let x = the number of flowers he picked from the lower trail.

Then 1000 – x = the number of flowers he picked from he upper trail. (The total number of flowers had to be 1000. Note that x plus 1000 – x does equal 1000.)

0.15x = the number of red flowers from the lower trail

0.35(1000 – x) = the number of red flowers from the upper trail.

0.20(1000) = the total number of red flowers desired. (That is 20% of 1000.)

The red flowers from the lower trail plus the red flowers from the upper trail has to equal the total number of red flowers desired.

$$0.15x + 0.35(1000 - x) = 0.20(1000)$$
$$0.15x + 350 - 0.35x = 200$$
$$-0.20x + 350 = 200$$
$$150 = 0.20x$$
$$750 = x$$

He should pick 750 wild flowers from the lower trail.

Using ② the Six Pretty boxes approach:

	red flowers picked	% that are red	no. of flowers
lower trail	0.15x	15%	x
upper trail	0.35(1000 – x)	35%	1000 – x

The Complete Solutions and Answers

6325. $x = \dfrac{-b \pm \sqrt{b^2 - 4ac}}{2a}$ becomes one number when $b^2 - 4ac$ is equal to zero. So you can just look at $4x^2 + 4x + 1 = 0$ and announce that there will be exactly one value of x that makes the equation true. Your friends will be impressed and ask how did you get to be so smart.

You can respond, "I just read it in a book, *videlicet, Zillions of Practice Problems Beginning Algebra.*"

6333. Darlene took a handful of dust off the television—it was 35% lint—and mixed it with a handful of dust off the chair—it was 75% lint.

She held 12 grams of Joe's dust that was 45% lint. How many grams had she taken off the television?

① First approach:

Let x = the number of grams of dust from the television.

Then 12 – x = the number of grams from the chair.

Then 0.35x = the number of grams of lint from the television dust.

Then 0.75(12 – x) = the number of grams of lint from the chair dust.

0.45(12) = the grams of lint she held in her hands.

$$0.35x + 0.75(12 - x) = 0.45(12)$$
$$0.35x + 9 - 0.75x = 5.4$$
$$-0.4x + 9 = 5.4$$
$$3.6 = 0.4x$$
$$9 = x \qquad \text{Dividing both sides by 0.4}$$

Darlene took 9 grams of dust off the television.

② The Six Pretty boxes approach:

	grams of lint	%	grams of dust
off the television	0.35x	35%	x
off the chair	0.75x(12 – x)	75%	12 – x

6344. The index of $\sqrt[3]{8xy}$ is 3.

Where there is no index number, such as in $\sqrt{29y}$, it is assumed to be 2.

The Complete Solutions and Answers

6405. Two cars start at the same spot. The red car heads west at 60 mph. The yellow car heads east at 50 mph. How long will it be before they are 660 miles apart?

❶ Using the Let t = . . . approach:

Let t = the number of hours that the cars travel.

Then 60t = the miles that the red car travels.

Then 50t = the miles that the yellow car travels.

Finally, since the total distance traveled by the two cars is 660 miles, the equation is

$$60t + 50t = 660$$

Adding $\quad\quad 110t = 660$

Dividing both sides by 110 $\quad\quad t = 6$

The cars each travel for 6 hours.

❷ Using the Six Pretty boxes approach:

	d	r	t
red car			t
yellow car			

→

	d	r	t
red car			t
yellow car			t

	d	r	t
red car		60	t
yellow car		50	t

→

	d	r	t
red car	60t	60	t
yellow car	50t	50	t

6408. If n is the first of three consecutive *odd* numbers, the next two are n + 2 and n + 4. Odd consecutive numbers are two apart from each other. For example, 4483, 4485 and 4487. If you add 2 to the first one, you will get the second one.

6411. A rectangle has a width of 9 inches and an area of 108 square inches. The formula for the area of a rectangle is $A = \ell w$ where ℓ is the length and w is the width.

So $A = \ell w$ becomes $108 = 9\ell$. (The coefficient always goes in front of the letter.) Dividing both sides by 9, we get $\frac{108}{9} = \ell$. Since $\frac{108}{9}$ equals 12, we have $\ell = 12$ inches.

The Complete Solutions and Answers

6414. Solve $\begin{cases} 2x + 5y = 35 \\ 5x + 9y = 77 \end{cases}$

If I choose to eliminate the y-terms, I will have to make them into 45y and −45y. Instead, I will eliminate the x-terms by making them into 10x and −10x. I do this because the numbers are smaller.

$$\begin{cases} 10x + 25y = 175 & \text{multiplying by 5} \\ -10x - 18y = -154 & \text{multiplying by } -2 \end{cases}$$

$$7y = 21 \quad \text{adding the two equations together}$$
$$y = 3$$

Substituting y = 3 into the first equation:
$$2x + 5(3) = 35$$
$$2x + 15 = 35$$
$$2x = 20$$
$$x = 10$$

The final answer is x = 10 and y = 3.

6417. There are many possibilities for three numbers whose mean average is 10. The easiest is 10, 10, 10.

Or 9, 10, 11.

Or 0, 10, 20.

Or any three numbers that add to 30.

6418. $5 < x < 6$ is true for $x = 5.01$ or $5\frac{1}{8}$ or 5.2 or $5\frac{2}{5}$ or $5 + \frac{1}{\pi}$ or $5\frac{11}{100}$ or 5.9999998932. Your answer may differ from mine.

6420. $5^{-2} = \dfrac{1}{5^2} = \dfrac{1}{25}$

6421. The coefficient of πx^4 is the number that goes in front of the letters (the variables). π is a number. The coefficient of πx^4 is π.
Pi is approximately equal to 3.14159265358979323846264338332795.

6424. $\{\, x \mid x$ is a real number that cannot be written as a/b where a and b are integers and $b \neq 0\}$ is the set of **irrational numbers**.

The Complete Solutions and Answers

6498. $4x + 6 \overline{)8x^3 + 12x + 77}$

The first step is to insert all the missing terms. There is no x^2 term in this case.

$$4x + 6 \overline{)8x^3 + 0x^2 + 12x + 77}$$

$4x$ goes into $8x^3$ $2x^2$ times.

That's true because $4x$ times $2x^2$ equals $8x^3$.

$$\begin{array}{r} 2x^2 \\ 4x + 6 \overline{)8x^3 + 0x^2 + 12x + 77} \end{array}$$

And, now like regular long division, you multiply $2x^2$ times $4x + 6$ and put your answer down below.

$$\begin{array}{r} 2x^2 \\ 4x + 6 \overline{)8x^3 + 0x^2 + 12x + 77} \\ \underline{8x^3 + 12x^2} \end{array}$$

And, now like regular division, you subtract and bring down the next term.

$$\begin{array}{r} 2x^2 \\ 4x + 6 \overline{)8x^3 + 0x^2 + 12x + 77} \\ \underline{8x^3 + 12x^2} \\ -12x^2 + 12x \end{array}$$

We now repeat the process. Divide $4x$ into $-12x^2$

$$\begin{array}{r} 2x^2 \ -3x \\ 4x + 6 \overline{)8x^3 + 0x^2 + 12x + 77} \\ \underline{8x^3 + 12x^2} \\ -12x^2 + 12x \end{array}$$

Multiply the $-3x$ times the $4x + 6$ and put your answer down below and then subtract. Then bring down the next term.

$$\begin{array}{r} 2x^2 \ -3x \\ 4x + 6 \overline{)8x^3 + 0x^2 + 12x + 77} \\ \underline{8x^3 + 12x^2} \\ -12x^2 + 12x \\ \underline{-12x^2 - 18x} \\ +30x + 77 \end{array}$$

> Here is where you can see why we did subtraction of negative numbers in the text.

The Complete Solutions and Answers

Then divide 4x into 30x. It goes 15/2 times.

Arithmetic review: $30 \div 4 = \dfrac{30}{4} = \dfrac{15}{2}$

$$
\begin{array}{r}
2x^2 \ -3x \ + 15/2 \\
4x + 6 \overline{)\ 8x^3 + \ 0x^2 + 12x + 77} \\
\underline{8x^3 + 12x^2} \\
-12x^2 + 12x \\
\underline{-12x^2 - 18x} \\
+ 30x \ + 77
\end{array}
$$

Multiply 15/2 by 4x + 6. Put your answer down below and subtract.

$$
\begin{array}{r}
2x^2 \ -3x \ + 15/2 \\
4x + 6 \overline{)\ 8x^3 + \ 0x^2 + 12x + 77} \\
\underline{8x^3 + 12x^2} \\
-12x^2 + 12x \\
\underline{-12x^2 - 18x} \\
+30x \ + 77 \\
\underline{+30x \ + 45} \\
32
\end{array}
$$

And then, just like long division, you put the remainder up as a fraction.

$$
\begin{array}{r}
1 \ + \tfrac{3}{4} \\
4\overline{)\ 7} \\
\underline{4} \\
3
\end{array}
$$

$$
\begin{array}{r}
2x^2 \ -3x \ + 15/2 \ + \frac{32}{4x + 6} \\
4x + 6 \overline{)\ 8x^3 + \ 0x^2 + 12x + 77} \\
\underline{8x^3 + 12x^2} \\
-12x^2 + 12x \\
\underline{-12x^2 - 18x} \\
+30x \ + 77 \\
\underline{+30x \ + 45} \\
32
\end{array}
$$

The Complete Solutions and Answers

6500. $-56/-8 = 7$ or $+7$ When the signs are alike, for multiplication or division, the answer is positive.

      Note: You cannot multiply three numbers together. The only thing you can do is multiply two numbers and then times the third.

      For example: $(5)(3)(10)$

$$= (15)(10)$$
$$= 150$$

6505. The radicand is the stuff under the radical sign. In this case, the radicand of $\sqrt{5432xyz}$ is 5432xyz. Don't you wish that all algebra questions were this easy?

6509. $\dfrac{y + \sqrt{z}}{\sqrt{z}}$

Multiply top and bottom by $\sqrt{z}$ which is the final answer, or you could multiply out the top if you wished.

$$\frac{(y + \sqrt{z})\sqrt{z}}{z}$$

$$\frac{y\sqrt{z} + z}{z}$$

6511. Solve $6x^2 + 4x + 3 = 0$

Let's first check $b^2 - 4ac$ to see if it is a perfect square. If it is, then the equation can be solved by factoring.

      $b^2 - 4ac = 16 - (4)(6)(3) = -56.$

      It's negative. That means that we will get the square root of a negative number when we use the quadratic formula.

      We are done. There are no real numbers, which when squared, will equal -56. There is no solution.

      For fun, if you put -56 in your calculator and hit the $\sqrt{}$ key, your calculator will scream ERROR! At least, that's what mine did.

6532. Factor $7x^2 - 63$

We always look for a common factor first.

      $7x^2 - 63 = 7(x^2 - 9) = 7(x + 3)(x - 3)$ (difference of squares)

The Complete Solutions and Answers

6685. { x | x is a movie star} is the set of all movie stars.

6702. $5(x + w) = 5x + 5w$ is an example of the distributive property.

6704. Darlene has some pancake mix that contains 2% sugar. She calls that her bitter mix. She has some that contains 5% sugar. She calls that her too-sweet mix.

She wants to make 60 pounds of pancake mix that has 3% sugar. How much of each mix should she use?

❶ Using the Let x = . . . approach:

Let x = the number of pounds of bitter mix used.

Then $60 - x$ = the number of pounds of too-sweet used. (Notice that x and $60 - x$ add to the desired 60 pounds of final product desired.)

Then $0.02x$ = the number of pounds of sugar contributed by the bitter mix.

Then $0.05(60 - x)$ = the number of pounds of sugar contributed by the too-sweet mix. (The too-sweet mix contributes $60 - x$ pounds containing 5% sugar.)

The final mixture will have 1.8 pounds of sugar in it. (The final mixture is 60 pounds of mix containing 3% sugar. $0.03 \times 60 = 1.8$.)

Finally, since the amount of sugar contributed by the bitter mix plus the amount of sugar contributed by the too-sweet mix is equal to 1.8, we have the equation:

$$0.02x + 0.05(60 - x) = 1.8$$
$$0.02x + 3 - 0.05x = 1.8 \qquad \text{distributive law}$$
$$-0.03x + 3 = 1.8 \qquad \text{combining } 0.02x \text{ and } -0.05x$$
$$3 = 1.8 + 0.03x \qquad \text{adding } 0.03x \text{ to both sides}$$
$$1.2 = 0.03x \qquad \text{subtracting 1.8 from both sides}$$
$$40 = x \qquad \text{dividing both sides by 0.03}$$

She used 40 pounds of bitter mix and 20 pounds of too-sweet mix. (The question asked for the amount of both mixes. Writing "40 pounds" does not answer the question.)

❷ Using the Six Pretty Boxes approach:

	sugar contributed	% sugar	pounds of mix
bitter mix	0.02x	2%	x
too-sweet mix	0.05(60 − x)	5%	60 − x

Usually, it is the last two boxes that you fill in that are used in creating the equation. **↞ Nice piece of information.**

The Complete Solutions and Answers

6711. One slice of Stanthony's Finest Combo Pizza weighs 2.8 pounds. The weight is proportional to the number of slices. Seven slices would weigh seven times as much a one slice. $7 \times 2.8 = 19.6$ pounds.

That's a big pizza!

6730. $10 + 20 / 40 = 10 + \frac{1}{2} = 10\frac{1}{2}$

6735. The median average of 7, 4, 3, 88, 555 is found by first putting the numbers in numerical order: 3, 4, 7, 88, 555. Then you pick the number in the middle. The median average is 7.

6738. The equality of two ratios is called a **proportion**.

For example: $\frac{2}{3} = \frac{x}{6}$

6742. $\dfrac{x^{-5}y^3}{x^2y^{-9}} = x^{-7}y^{12}$ or $\dfrac{y^{12}}{x^7}$

In Chapter 1, we learned subtraction of integers. In that chapter we did problems like: $-5 - (+2)$ and $3 - (-9)$.

Now here in Chapter 6, we are actively using that knowledge.

6748. Name three consecutive odd numbers that add to 1881.

The first step in any word problem is to "Let x = . . ." the thing you are trying to find out. In this case, we are trying to find three different numbers.

So we will let x = the first number.

Then x + 2 = the next consecutive odd number.

Then x + 4 = the third of the three consecutive odd numbers.

We are told that their sum is 1881, so we have the equation:

$$x + x + 2 + x + 4 = 1881$$
$$3x + 6 = 1881$$
$$3x = 1875 \qquad \text{subtracting 6 from both sides}$$
$$x = 625 \qquad \text{dividing both sides by 3}$$

The three numbers are x, x + 2, and x + 4, which in this case are 625, 627, and 629.

The Complete Solutions and Answers

6800. $0^1 = 0$.   Anything raised to the first power is equal to itself.
$3,000,000^1 = 3,000,000$

$1^0 = 1$ Any (non-zero) number raised to the zero power is equal to one.

Therefore $0^1 < 1^0$.

6811. Is every natural number a rational number?

The natural numbers are $\{1, 2, 3, 4, \ldots\}$.

The rational numbers are any number that can be expressed as $\frac{a}{b}$ where a and b are integers and $b \neq 0$.

Take a natural number, say, 45889. Can it be expressed as $\frac{a}{b}$ where a and b are integers and $b \neq 0$?

Yes. 45889 can be written as $\frac{45889}{1}$

Every natural number is a rational number.

6825. $\dfrac{\sqrt{x} + \sqrt{y}}{\sqrt{x} - \sqrt{y}}$

Multiply the top and bottom by the conjugate
of the bottom which is $\sqrt{x} + \sqrt{y}$

$\dfrac{(\sqrt{x} + \sqrt{y})(\sqrt{x} + \sqrt{y})}{(\sqrt{x} - \sqrt{y})(\sqrt{x} + \sqrt{y})} = \dfrac{(\sqrt{x} + \sqrt{y})(\sqrt{x} + \sqrt{y})}{x - y}$ which is the

final answer. Or you could multiply out the top and get $\dfrac{x + 2\sqrt{xy} + y}{x - y}$

6831. $3x + 2 \overline{)6x^3 - 5x^2}$

Put in the missing terms $(0x + 0)$
and then have fun with the division.

$$
\begin{array}{r}
2x^2 - 3x + 2 + \frac{-4}{3x+2} \\
3x + 2 \overline{)\ 6x^3 - 5x^2 + 0x + 0} \\
\underline{6x^3 + 4x^2} \\
-9x^2 + 0x \\
\underline{-9x^2 - 6x} \\
+ 6x + 0 \\
\underline{6x + 4} \\
- 4
\end{array}
$$

The Complete Solutions and Answers

6902. Solve by substitution $\begin{cases} y = 5x + 2 \\ 6x + 2y = 52 \end{cases}$

To solve by substitution, first take either equation and solve for one of the variables. In this problem, that's already been done: $y = 5x + 2$.

The value of y is $5x + 2$.

Substitute that value into the other equation: $6x + 2(5x + 2) = 52$.

We now have one equation with one unknown.

distributive property	$6x + 10x + 4 = 52$
combine	$16x + 4 = 52$
subtract 4 from both sides	$16x = 48$
divide both sides by 16	$x = 3$

Substitute $x = 3$ back into any equation containing both x and y.
In this case, the first equation is the easiest. $y = 5(3) + 2$.

$$y = 17$$

The final answer is $x = 3$ and $y = 17$.

6924. Line 1 told us that *every number* multiplied by zero gives an answer of zero.

Line 2 told us that $\frac{7}{0}$ multiplied by zero doesn't give us an answer of zero.

Therefore, (Line 3), $\frac{7}{0}$ can't be a number. It's that simple.

6955. Example A is not a function since C does not have exactly one image in the codomain. (It has no image in the codomain.)

Example B is a function. Each element in the domain has exactly one image in the codomain. (Example B is an example of a constant function.)

Example C is a function. Each element in the domain has exactly one image in the codomain. (It doesn't matter that % isn't "hit" by any element in the domain.)

The Complete Solutions and Answers

7020. Among my 96 friends, for every 3 friends who like red as their favorite color, there are 7 who like blue, and 2 who like green. How many of them like green?

How many of these 96 friends like green as their favorite color?

Step One: 3:7:2

Step Two: 3x:7x:2x

Step Three: $3x + 7x + 2x = 96$

Then solve the equation: $\quad 12x = 96$

$\quad\quad\quad\quad\quad\quad\quad\quad\quad\quad x = 8 \quad$ dividing both sides by 12

The question asks for the number who like green. That is represented by 2x.

If $x = 8$, then $2x = 16$ who like green.

7023. The coefficient of x^{20} is the same as the coefficient of $1x^{20}$. The coefficient is 1.

7030. $(532a^{32987}b^{-3}cd^{3.53}e^{-1})^0 = 1$

Any number raised to the "0"y power equals one.

7041. If n is the last of four consecutive numbers, the first three are $n - 3$, $n - 2$, and $n - 1$. For example, if $n = 60$, then $n - 3$ would be 57, $n - 2$ would be 58, and $n - 1$ would be 59.

7103. A table has a diameter of 56 inches. Since $C = \pi d$ and we are told to use $\frac{22}{7}$ for π, we have $C = \frac{22}{7} d = \frac{22}{7} \times 56 = \frac{22}{7} \times \frac{56}{1} =$

$\frac{22}{\cancel{7}} \times \frac{\cancel{56}^{8}}{1} = 22 \times 8 = 176$ inches.

7105. $\{ x \mid x + 4 = 7 \}$ is the set of all numbers that when added to 4 give an answer of 7. That could be written as $\{3\}$.

The Complete Solutions and Answers

7116. $2^6 = 64$

$6^2 = 36$ $\qquad\qquad$ $2^6 > 6^2$

7120. Darlene is hard on shoes. She wears them out very quickly. She wears out her dress shoes at the rate of 5/month. She wears out her sneakers at the rate of 3/month.

When she turned 16, she started wearing dress shoes. After several months, she switched over and started just wearing sneakers.

When she had worn sneakers for six more months than she wore dress shoes, she had worn out the same number of each. How long did she wear dress shoes?

❶ Using the Let x = . . . approach:

Let x = the number of months she wore dress shoes.

Then x + 6 = the number of months she wore sneakers. (She wore sneakers for six more months than she wore dress shoes.)

Then 5x = the number of dress shoes that she wore out. (She wore out dress shoes at the rate of 5/month for x months.)

Then 3(x + 6) = the number of sneakers that she wore out. (She wore out sneakers at the rate of 3/month for x + 6 months.)

Since she wore out the same number of dress shoes as sneakers, we have the equation: $\qquad$ $5x = 3(x + 6)$

$$5x = 3x + 18$$
$$2x = 18$$
$$x = 9$$

She wore dress shoes for 9 months.

❷ Using the Six Pretty Boxes approach:

	number of shoes	rate	months
dress shoes	5x	5/month	x
sneakers	3(x + 6)	3/month	x + 6

7225. $\sqrt[3]{64} = 4$, since $4^3 = 64$.

When the index is equal to two, such as in $\sqrt{100}$, we are automatically dealing with the **principal square root**. The answer must be non-negative.

But when the index is not equal to two, there are fewer restrictions. For example, we can take cube roots of negative numbers. $\sqrt[3]{-27}$ is equal to –3, since $(-3)^3 = -27$.

In fact, the cube root of a negative number is always negative.

The Complete Solutions and Answers

7304. A rectangle has a width of 5.4 yards and an area of 45.9 yards. Substituting these numbers in the area formula $A = \ell w$, we obtain $45.9 = 5.4\ell$. Dividing both sides by 5.4, $\frac{45.9}{5.4} = \ell$.

$$5.4\overline{)45.9} \quad \Rightarrow \quad 54.\overline{)459.0} \quad \text{so } \ell = 8.5 \text{ yards}$$
$$\begin{array}{r} 8.5 \\ 54.\overline{)459.0} \\ -432 \\ \hline 270 \\ -270 \end{array}$$

7306. $(xyz^6)^4 = x^4y^4z^{24}$

7309. Express without negative exponents $\dfrac{x^{-5}y}{x^6y^{-4}} = x^{-11}y^5 = \dfrac{y^5}{x^{11}}$

7333. Darlene bought a new fondue pot. She filled it with melted chocolate and set out a bowl of giant strawberries to dip in the chocolate.

Joe ate the chocolate strawberries three times as fast as Darlene. In 6 minutes, they had consumed 12 strawberries. How fast was Darlene eating them?

Let r = the rate Darlene was eating the strawberries.

Then 3r = the rate Joe was consuming the strawberries.

Then 6r = the number of strawberries Darlene ate. (She ate them at the rate of r for 6 minutes.)

Then 3r(6) = the number of strawberries Joe ate. (He ate them at the rate of 3r for 6 minutes.)

$$6r + 3r(6) = 12$$
$$6r + 18r = 12$$
$$24r = 12$$
$$r = \frac{1}{2} \text{ (or 0.5, if you prefer)}$$

Darlene ate them at the rate of one-half strawberry per minute.

Using the Six Pretty boxes approach:

	strawberries eaten	rate	time
Darlene	6r	r	6
Joe	3r(6)	3r	6

238

The Complete Solutions and Answers

7403. $(5x + 3)(4x + 7) = 20x^2 + 35x + 12x + 21 = 20x^2 + 47x + 21$

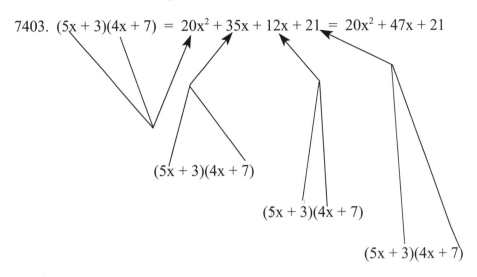

$(5x + 3)(4x + 7)$

$(5x + 3)(4x + 7)$

$(5x + 3)(4x + 7)$

7412. If the index of a radical is 4, can the radicand be negative?

This would be something like $\sqrt[4]{-16}$.

If $\sqrt[4]{-16}$ were equal to some number x, then x^4 would have to equal -16.

But any real number to the fourth power can never be negative.

If the index of a radical is 4, the radicand can never be negative.

7425. Solve $3 = \sqrt{x - 7}$

There are three steps in solving an equation with radicals:

      1. Isolate the radical on one side of the equation.

      2. Square both sides.

      3. Check each answer in the original equation.

The radical is already on one side of the equation all by itself, so step 1 has already been done. $3 = \sqrt{x - 7}$ step one done

    Square both sides $9 = x - 7$

> If we square something that has been square rooted, then we get back the original expression.
> $(\sqrt{m})^2 = m$

$16 = x$

The last step is to check the answer in the original problem.

$3 \overset{?}{=} \sqrt{16 - 7}$ Yes. That is true. $x = 16$ is the final answer.

The Complete Solutions and Answers

7606. $(8y + 2)(3y - 9) = 24y^2 - 72y + 6y - 18 = 24y^2 - 66y - 18$

7700. A red mouse can eat all the turnovers in my pantry in 6 hours. A blue mouse can eat them all in 6 hours. A green mouse can eat them all in 3 hours. If all three work on my turnovers, how soon would they all be gone?

Let x = the number of hours it would take the three mice to eat all the turnovers.

Then $\frac{1}{x}$ is the part of the turnovers they can eat in one hour.

Since the red mouse can eat all of them in 6 hours, he can eat $\frac{1}{6}$ of them in one hour.

Same for the blue mouse.

Since the green mouse can eat all of them in 3 hours, he can eat $\frac{1}{3}$ of them in one hour.

$$\frac{1}{6} + \frac{1}{6} + \frac{1}{3} = \frac{1}{x}$$

The least common denominator is 6x. Each of the denominators can divide evenly into 6x. We multiply each term of this fractional equation by 6x. $\frac{1(6x)}{6} + \frac{1(6x)}{6} + \frac{1(6x)}{3} = \frac{1(6x)}{x}$

The fractions disappear.

$$x + x + 2x = 6$$
$$4x = 6$$
$$x = \frac{6}{4} = 1\frac{1}{2} \text{ hours.}$$

7777. The next consecutive number that comes after n is n + 1.

7788. $z^2 z^4 z^3 = z^9$

7790. A ball with a diameter of 8" has a radius of 4".
The formula for the volume of a sphere is $V = (4/3)\pi r^3$.
In this problem, $V = (4/3)(3)(4^3) = 256$ cubic inches.

7791. The easiest example I can think of would be to let a = 1. There are many more possible.

The Complete Solutions and Answers

7792. There are several different ways that {100, 101, 102, ..., 996, 997, 998, 999} could be written using set builder notation.

For example, { x | x is a three-digit natural number} or
{ x | x is a natural number such that $100 \leq x \leq 999$} or
{ x | x is a natural number such that $99 < x < 1000$} or
{ y | y is a natural number such that $100 \leq y \leq 999$} or
{ z | z is a natural number such that $100 \leq z \leq 999$}.

      In all of the above examples, x, y and z are called "dummy variables." When you eliminate the set builder notation, in every case the x, y and z disappear and all you have is {100, 101, 102, ..., 996, 997, 998, 999}.

      I could have even used my favorite Greek letter ξ (pronounced "xi") and expressed {100, 101, 102, ..., 996, 997, 998, 999} as
{ ξ | ξ is a natural number such that $100 \leq \xi \leq 999$}.

      If your favorite friend's name is Pat, you could have written
{ p | p is a natural number such that $100 \leq p \leq 999$}.

7800. Graph $y = 0.5x^2$.

If x = 0, then y = 0.	We plot (0, 0).
If x = 1, then y = 0.5.	We plot (1, 0.5).
If x = 2, then y = 2.	We plot (2, 2).
If x = −2, then y = 2.	We plot (−2, 2).

We notice that a positive value of x and the corresponding negative value of x will give the same y.

If x = ±3, then y = 4.5.	We plot (3, 4.5) and (−3, 4.5).
If x = ±4, then y = 8.	We plot (4, 8) and (−4, 8).

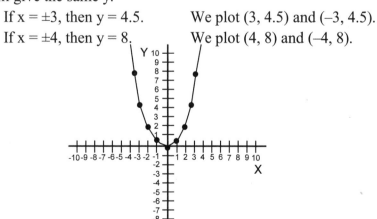

The Complete Solutions and Answers

7803. Solve $6x = \dfrac{10}{x} + 7$

If it helps, you can make them all into fractions, but many people don't need to do that.

$$\frac{6x}{1} = \frac{10}{x} + \frac{7}{1}$$

The smallest expression that 1, x, and 1 divide evenly into is x. Multiplying each term by x:

$$6x^2 = 10 + 7x$$

$6x^2 - 7x - 10 = 0$ Transpose everything to one side.

$6x^2 - 12x + 5x - 10 = 0$ Find two things that multiply to $-60x^2$ and
                                  add to $-7x$.

$6x(x - 2) + 5(x - 2) = 0$ Factoring by grouping

$(x - 2)(6x + 5) = 0$

$x - 2 = 0$ OR $6x + 5 = 0$

$x = 2$ OR $x = -5/6$

Rule: If you multiply an equation by an expression containing a variable, you must check you answer(s) back in the original problem.

Checking $x = 2$ is easy: $12 \overset{?}{=} 5 + 7$ yes.

Checking $x = -5/6$ is going to take some arithmetic. Arithmetic can be more work than algebra.

$$6(-5/6) \overset{?}{=} \frac{10}{(-5/6)} + 7$$

$$\frac{6}{1} \times \frac{-5}{6} \overset{?}{=} \frac{10}{1} \times \frac{-6}{5} + 7$$

$$-5 \overset{?}{=} -12 + 7 \qquad \text{yes}$$

The final answer is $x = 2$ or $x = -5/6$.

7814. $\dfrac{w^7}{x^{-3} - z^4} = \dfrac{w^7}{(1/x^3) - z^4}$

$$= \frac{x^3 w^7}{1 - x^3 z^4}$$ We multiplied the top and bottom by x^3 in order to eliminate the complex fraction.

7815. $-\sqrt{36} = -6$

Note that $\sqrt{36}$ only equals 6 and not ±6, since $\sqrt{}$ indicates the principal square root of a number. Hence, $-\sqrt{36} = -6$.

The Complete Solutions and Answers

8000. $8 \cdot 4 + 2 = 32 + 2 = 34$

8004. Stanthony's medium pizza is 21" in diameter. Since $C = \pi d$ and d is equal to 21 and we are using 22/7 for π, we have $C = \dfrac{22}{7} \times \dfrac{21}{1} =$

$\dfrac{22}{\cancel{7}} \times \dfrac{\cancel{21}^{\,3}}{1} = 66$ inches.

8008. Solve $\dfrac{y}{y+1} - \dfrac{3}{y+1} = \dfrac{4}{y^2+y}$

In order to find the smallest expression that $y + 1$ and $y^2 + y$ divide evenly into, you need to factor each of the denominators.

$$\frac{y}{y+1} - \frac{3}{y+1} = \frac{4}{y(y+1)}$$

Now we can see that the smallest expression that these denominators divide evenly into is $y(y + 1)$.

Multiplying each term by $y(y + 1)$:

$$\frac{(y)\mathbf{y(y+1)}}{y+1} - \frac{(3)\mathbf{y(y+1)}}{y+1} = \frac{(4)\mathbf{y(y+1)}}{y(y+1)}$$

No more fractions! $y^2 \qquad - \qquad 3y \qquad = 4$

Put everything on the left side $y^2 - 3y - 4 = 0$

Factor (two numbers that multiply

to –4 and add to – 3) $(y - 4)(y + 1) = 0$

$$y - 4 = 0 \;\; OR \;\; y + 1 = 0$$
$$y = 4 \;\; OR \;\; y = -1$$

Rule: If you multiply an equation by an expression containing a variable, you must check you answer(s) back in the original problem.

checking $y = 4$

$\dfrac{4}{5} - \dfrac{3}{5} \overset{?}{=} \dfrac{4}{20}$

$\dfrac{4}{5} - \dfrac{3}{5} \overset{?}{=} \dfrac{1}{5}$ yes

checking $y = -1$

$\dfrac{-1}{0} - \ldots$ Stop right here.

Division by zero is not permitted.

$y = -1$ does not check.

The final answer is $y = 4$.

8009. $\sqrt{90} + \sqrt{50} + \sqrt{160}$

$= \sqrt{9}\,\sqrt{10} + \sqrt{25}\,\sqrt{2} + \sqrt{16}\,\sqrt{10}$

$= 3\sqrt{10} + 5\sqrt{2} + 4\sqrt{10} \;=\; 7\sqrt{10} + 5\sqrt{2}$

The Complete Solutions and Answers

8207. In 58 minutes, Joe can wash 3 cars and 4 dogs. In 99 minutes, he can wash 5 cars and 7 dogs. How long does it take him to wash a car, and how long does it take him to wash a dog?

Let x = the number of minutes it takes Joe to wash a car.

Let y = the number of minutes it takes Joe to wash a dog.

$$\begin{cases} 3x + 4y = 58 \\ 5x + 7y = 99 \end{cases}$$

If I want to eliminate the x variables, I will make them 15x and $-15x$. If I want to eliminate the y variables, I will make them 28y and $-28y$. It looks like it will be easier to eliminate the x variables. (Going either way will gave the same answer.)

Multiplying the first equation by 5 and the second by -3:

$$\begin{cases} 15x + 20y = 290 \\ -15x - 21y = -297 \end{cases}$$

Adding the two equations $-y = -7$

Multiplying by -1 $y = 7$

Substituting y = 7 into the first equation

$$3x + 4(7) = 58$$
$$3x + 28 = 58$$
$$3x = 30$$
$$x = 10$$

It takes 10 minutes for Joe to wash a car and 7 minutes to wash a dog.

8210.

$$\frac{x^{-2} + y^{-3}}{z^6} = \frac{\dfrac{1}{x^2} + \dfrac{1}{y^3}}{z^6}$$

Multiplying top and bottom by x^2y^3 to eliminate the complex fraction

$$= \frac{\dfrac{x^2y^3}{x^2} + \dfrac{x^2y^3}{y^3}}{x^2y^3z^6}$$

$$= \frac{y^3 + x^2}{x^2y^3z^6}$$

OR you could have simply taken the original fraction and multiplied top and bottom by x^2y^3 and gotten the final answer in one step.

8212. The index of $\sqrt{34vwxyz}$ is 2

For radicals with higher indexes such as 3, we write the number.

For example, $\sqrt[3]{}$ or $\sqrt[8]{}$. But when the index is 2, we just write $\sqrt{}$.

The Complete Solutions and Answers

8327. Joe and Darlene start a dog-washing business. They wash dogs in Darlene's bathtub. Joe started washing dogs at the rate of 8 dogs/hour. Then Darlene took over and started washing them at the rate of 12 dogs/hour while Joe watched television. She worked for 3 more hours than Joe had worked. Together they washed a total of 46 dogs. How long did Joe work?

❶   Let t = the number of hours Joe worked.

Then t + 3 = the number of hours Darlene worked.

Then 8t = the number of dogs Joe washed. (He washed dogs at the rate of 8 dogs/hour for t hours.)

Then 12(t + 3) = the number of dogs Darlene washed. (She washed at the rate of 12 dogs/hour for t + 3 hours.)

Finally, since they washed a total of 46 dogs, we have the equation:

$$8t + 12(t + 3) = 46$$

$8t + 12t + 36 = 46$	Distributive property
$20t + 36 = 46$	Adding
$20t = 10$	Subtracting 36 from both sides of the equation
$t = \dfrac{10}{20}$	Dividing both sides by 20

Joe worked for $\dfrac{1}{2}$ hour.   ($\dfrac{10}{20}$ is equal to $\dfrac{1}{2}$)

❷

	dogs	dogs/hour	hours
Joe			t
Darlene			

→

	dogs	dogs/hour	hours
Joe			t
Darlene			t + 3

	dogs	dogs/hour	hours
Joe		8	t
Darlene		12	t + 3

→

	dogs	dogs/hour	hours
Joe	8t	8	t
Darlene	12(t + 3)	12	t + 3

8329. To see Roger, you would have to walk half way around the world. If the diameter is 8,000 miles, then the circumference is $C = \pi d \approx 3d = (3)(8000) = 24{,}000$ miles. So half way around would be 12,000 miles.

8332. If n is the last of three consecutive even numbers, the first two are n – 4 and n – 2.

The Complete Solutions and Answers

8340. If you have, for example, 3, 8, 10, 56, and you are asked to find the median average, the usual procedure is to pick the two numbers in the middle of the list and take the mean average of those two numbers.

The median average of 3, 8, 10, 56 is the mean average of 8 and 10 which is $\dfrac{8+10}{2} = 9$.

8411. $\dfrac{1}{2} \geq \dfrac{1}{2}$ is true. Every number is $\geq$ itself.

$\dfrac{1}{4} \leq \dfrac{1}{8}$ is false. $\dfrac{1}{4} > \dfrac{1}{8}$ since $0.25 > 0.125$

$\dfrac{1}{5} > \dfrac{1}{6}$ is true. $0.2 > 0.1666...$

$-\dfrac{1}{5} > -\dfrac{1}{6}$ is false. $-\dfrac{1}{6}$ is closer to zero than $-\dfrac{1}{5}$ and hence $-\dfrac{1}{5}$ is to the left of $-\dfrac{1}{6}$ on the number line.

8413. $12 / 6 \cdot 2 = 2 \cdot 2 = 4$ Multiplication and division are done left to right.

8416. A bouquet of 3 daisies and 9 carnations cost \$33. A bouquet of 4 daisies and 7 carnations cost \$29. How much does each flower cost?

Let x = the cost of one daisy.

Let y = the cost of one carnation.

$$\begin{cases} 3x + 9y = 33 \\ 4x + 7y = 29 \end{cases}$$

If I were trying to eliminate the y variable, I would have to multiply the first equation by 7 and the second equation by –9. That's too much work.

Instead, there is less work if I eliminate the x variable.

Multiply the first equation by 4 and the second by –3.

$$\begin{cases} 12x + 36y = 132 \\ -12x - 21y = -87 \end{cases}$$

$15y = 45$ adding the two equations

$y = 3$

Substituting y = 3 into the second equation: $4x + 7(3) = 29$

$4x + 21 = 29$

$4x = 8$

$x = 2$

Daisies are \$2 and carnations are \$3.

The Complete Solutions and Answers

8418. $(6x^2y^{-3})^5 = 6^5x^{10}y^{-15}$ or $\dfrac{6^5x^{10}}{y^{15}}$

8695. Name three consecutive numbers that add to 138.

The first step in almost any word problem is to write, "Let n = *the thing you are trying to find out*." (Or you could write Let x = . . . or Let t = . . . depending on the kind of thing you are trying to find out.)

    Let n = the first of the three consecutive numbers.

After writing the "Let n = . . . " you write "Then *some expression* = . . ." on the basis of that "Let n = . . ." statement you just wrote. This is almost always **the second step in solving a word problem**.

    I notice that *n = the first of the three consecutive numbers* allows me to write:

    Then n + 1 = the second of the three consecutive numbers.

    Then n + 2 = the third of the three consecutive numbers.

When you have written enough of those "Then . . . " statements, the equation will almost fall into your lap.

    Important point: To solve word problems, you can not just jump from the English to the equation.

    My thinking: *If n is the first and n+1 is the second, and n+2 is the third, and I am told that the sum is 138, then the equation is* . . .

$$n + (n + 1) + (n + 2) = 138$$

Then solve the equation.

$$3n + 3 = 138$$

        subtract 3 from both sides $3n = 135$

        divide both sides by 3 $n = 45$

    That's not the end of the problem. The question was, "Name three consecutive numbers that add to 138."
The first is n = 45. The second is n + 1 = 46. The third is n + 2 = 47.

    It's often nice to check your work. Let's see if 45, 46, and 47 is really the answer:

    ☞ Are they consecutive? 45, 46, and 47 are consecutive.

    ☞ Do they add to 138? 45 + 46 + 47 do add to 138.

8700. $100^{-1/2} = \dfrac{1}{100^{1/2}} = \dfrac{1}{\sqrt{100}} = \dfrac{1}{10}$

The Complete Solutions and Answers

8870. The army van heads south from KITTENS University at 30 mph. Four hours later, Betty and Alexander head south from KITTENS University chasing the army van. They are going 50 mph. How long will it take Betty and Alexander to catch up with the army van?

☞☞☞ Let t = the number of hours it will take them to catch up. ☜☜☜ Important! This is the way you start almost all word problems. You let the variable (t or x or n or whatever) equal the thing you are trying to find out. That is the first step.

After writing the "Let t = . . . " you write "Then *some bunch of letters* = . . ." on the basis of that "Let t = . . ." statement you just wrote. This is almost always **the second step in solving a word problem**.

Then t + 4 = the number of hours the van was driven (since t = the number of hours it will take Betty and Alexander to catch up, and the army van left four hours before they did).

Then 50t = the number of miles that Betty and Alexander drove (since Betty and Alexander drove t hours at 50 mph).

Then 30(t + 4) = the number of miles the army van drove (since the army van drove t + 4 hours at 30 mph).

Finally, 50t = 30(t + 4) (since when Betty and Alexander catch up with the army van they will have both driven the same distance).

Solving the equation	50t = 30(t + 4)
By the distributive property	50t = 30t + 120
Subtract 30t from both sides	20t = 120
Divide both sides by 20	t = 6

It took Betty and Alexander 6 hours to catch up.

8888. The cardinality of {7, 8, 9} is 3. The cardinality of a set is the number of elements in that set.

8895. { x | x times x equals 25} is the set of all numbers that when multiplied by themselves give an answer of 25. Certainly 5 is in that set. But note that −5 is also in that set, since (−5)(−5) = 25. The answer is {5, −5}.

The answer could also have been written as {−5, 5}. The order in which you list the elements of a set does not matter.

8898. $7(8x + 9y) = 56x + 63y$

The Complete Solutions and Answers

8900. Four people are on the bus. One of them is carrying $1000. The mean average of what those four people are carrying is $250. How much are the other three people carrying?

We want $\dfrac{? + ? + ? + 1000}{4}$ to equal 250.

No one is carrying a negative amount of money. The only way that $\dfrac{? + ? + ? + 1000}{4} = 250$ is if the other three people are not carrying any money at all.

8912. The roses, daisies, and marigolds are in the continued ratio 5:6:9 with a total of 120 of these plants.

Step One: 5:6:9

Step Two: 5x:6x:9x

Step Three: 5x + 6x + 9x = 120

Then solve the equation: 20x = 120

x = 6 (dividing both sides by 20)

The question asks for the number of daisies. That is represented by the 6x.

If x = 6, then 6x = 36 daisies. (multiplying both sides by 6)

8915. If (c, d) is directly above (6, 7), the c must be equal to 6. The d must be greater than 7.

8919. $100^{-2} = \dfrac{1}{100^2} = \dfrac{1}{10,000}$

8950. The area of a trapezoid is $A = \frac{1}{2} h(a + b)$.

The lengths of the parallel sides are 9 and 15 feet, and the distance between the parallel sides is 7 feet. So $A = \frac{1}{2} (7)(9 + 15) = \frac{1}{2} (7)(24) = 84$ square feet.

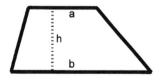

8952.   Let x = 0.907907907907. . . .

Then 1000x = 907.907907907907. . . .

Subtracting: 999x = 907

Dividing: $x = \dfrac{907}{999}$

The Complete Solutions and Answers

8970. Joe walked from his apartment to the ice cream store at 4 ft/sec. When he got to the store he realized that he had left his money at home and walked back to his apartment at 3 ft/sec. He walked for a total of 280 seconds to and from the store. How long did it take him to walk to the store?

❶ Using the Let t = approach:

Let t = the number of seconds it took Joe to walk to the store.
Then 280 – t = the number of seconds it took Joe to walk from the store back to his apartment. This is something new to this chapter.

We know that the whole round trip took 280 seconds. We know that the trip to the store took t seconds. How long did it take him to go from the store to his apartment?

Let's do some examples:

If it took 20 seconds to go to the store, it would have taken 260 seconds to come back home.
If it took 100 seconds to go to the store, it would have taken 180 seconds to come back home.
If it took 270 seconds to go to the store, it would have taken 10 seconds to come back home.
(We are subtracting from 280, aren't we?)
If it took t seconds to go to the store, it would have taken 280 – t seconds to come back home.

Whenever you are in doubt as to whether it's addition, subtraction, multiplication, or division, take some simple numbers and then look and see what you are doing.

Then 4t = the number of feet to the store. (4 ft/sec for t seconds.)

Then 3(280 – t) = the number of feet from the store back to his apartment. (Joe was going at 3 ft/sec for 280 – t seconds.)

Finally, since the distance to the store is equal to the distance from the store back to his apartment, we have the equation:

$$4t = 3(280 - t)$$
$$4t = 840 - 3t \qquad \text{Using the distributive law}$$
$$7t = 840 \qquad \text{Adding 3t to both sides of the equation}$$
$$t = 120 \qquad \text{Dividing both sides by 7}$$

So it took Joe 120 seconds to walk to the ice cream store.

❷ Using the Six Pretty Boxes approach:

	distance	rate	time
to the store			t
back to apt.			

→

	distance	rate	time
to the store			t
back to apt.			280 – t

	distance	rate	time
to the store		4	t
back to apt.		3	280 – t

→

	distance	rate	time
to the store	4t	4	t
back to apt.	3(280–t)	3	280 – t

The Complete Solutions and Answers

8973. { x | x = 2n where n is a natural number} is the set of all numbers that can be written as twice some natural number. Using braces this would be written as {2, 4, 6, 8, 10, 12, . . . }.

8975. You are a veterinarian and you need to give a marten a shot to ease its pain. You need to give it 9 cc that contains 6% morphine. You have some 4% and some 10%. How much of each should you mix together?

❶   Let x = the cc of 4% used.

      Then 9 − x = the cc of 10% used.

      Then 0.04x = the amount of morphine contributed by the 4% solution.

      Then 0.1(9 − x) = the amount of morphine contributed by 10% solution.

      We want $0.06 \times 9 = 0.54$ cc of morphine.

      Finally, the equation is $0.04x + 0.1(9 − x) = 0.54$ (The amount of morphine contributed by each of the solutions has to equal the amount of morphine in the final answer.)

distributive law	$0.04x + 0.9 − 0.1x = 0.54$
combine	$−0.06x + 0.9 = 0.54$
add 0.06x to both sides	$0.9 = 0.54 + 0.06x$
subtract 0.54 from both sides	$0.36 = 0.06x$
divide both sides by 0.06	$6 = x$

Use 6 cc of the 4% and 3 cc of the 10%.

❷ Using Six Pretty Boxes:

	morphine	percent	cc of solution
weak solution	0.04x	4%	x
strong solution	0.1(9 − x)	10%	9 − x

These two need to add to 0.54.

8977. The mode average of 7, 7, 7, 7, 7, 7, 7, 7, 7, 7, 7, 7, 7, 7, 7, 8 is 7. The median average of 7, 7, 7, 7, 7, 7, 7, 7, 7, 7, 7, 7, 7, 7, 7, 8 is 7. The mean average of 7, 7, 7, 7, 7, 7, 7, 7, 7, 7, 7, 7, 7, 7, 7, 8 is slightly more than 7. Therefore the mean average is largest.

The Complete Solutions and Answers

8989. Using the Six Pretty Boxes approach, solve: The army van heads south from KITTENS University at 30 mph. Four hours later, Betty and Alexander head south from KITTENS University chasing the army van. They are going 50 mph. How long will it take Betty and Alexander to catch up with the army van?

This is a d = rt (distance equals rate times time) problem.

Count how many different quantities are involved. I count six of them: two driving speeds,

two lengths of time, and

two distances.

We fill in six pretty boxes:

	d	r	t
Betty & Alexander			
Army van			

Filling in boxes is, perhaps, easier than writing "*Then*" statements.

What do we want to find out? Put an x (or a *t*) in that box:

	d	r	t
Betty & Alexander			t
Army van			

We know the army van was driven 4 hours longer:

	d	r	t
Betty & Alexander			t
Army van			$t+4$

We know the two speeds:

	d	r	t
Betty & Alexander		50	t
Army van		30	$t+4$

The Complete Solutions and Answers

Since d = rt, we can fill in the last two boxes:

	d	r	t
Betty & Alexander	$50t$	50	t
Army van	$30(t+4)$	30	$t+4$

Since Betty & Alexander drove the same distance as the army van:
$$50t = 30(t+4)$$

then $50t = 30t + 120 \Rightarrow 20t = 120 \Rightarrow t = 6$

It took Betty and Alexander 6 hours to catch up with the army van.

9000. A linear equation is any equation that can be put in the form ax + by = c where a, b, and c are any numbers. (a and b are not both zero.)

This definition says *can be put in the form*, not *is in the form*.

5x = 7y + 3 is not in the form ax + by = c, but by transposing the 7y, it can be put into the form 5x – 7y = 3, which shows that 5x = 7y + 3 is a linear equation.

9009. $(-6)(+9) = -54$ Signs different ⇨ Answer negative

$(+8)(-8)(-10) = (-64)(-10) = +640$

$(-2)(-2)(-2)(-2)(-2) = (+4)(-2)(-2)(-2)$

$\qquad\qquad\qquad = (-8)(-2)(-2)$

$\qquad\qquad\qquad = (+16)(-2)$

$\qquad\qquad\qquad = -32$

9011. On the graph of y = –4 all the ordinates must be equal to –4.

If x = 0, then y = –4.
If x = 1, then y = –4.
If x = anything, then y = –4.

The Complete Solutions and Answers

9012. $\dfrac{a^{55}b^{20}c}{a^{33}b^{30}c} = a^{22}b^{-10}$ or $\dfrac{a^{22}}{b^{10}}$

9065. Darlene and Joe rented an airplane. Darlene piloted the plane at 600 mph and the rest of the time Joe flew it at 400 mph. They each flew the same distance and were in the air for a combined total of 10 hours. How long did Darlene pilot the plane?

❶ Using the Let t = approach:

Let t = the number of hours Darlene piloted the plane.

Then 10 – t = the number of hours that Joe piloted the plane.

(Notice that the sum of Darlene's hours (t) and Joe's hours (10 – t) equals 10.)

Then 600t = the number of miles Darlene flew the plane. (She flew at 600 mph for t hours.)

Then 400(10 – t) = the number of miles that Joe flew the plane. (He flew at 400 mph for 10 – t hours.)

Finally, since they flew the same distance, we have the equation:

$$600t = 400(10 - t)$$

$600t = 4000 - 400t$	distributive law
$1000t = 4000$	add 400t to both sides
$t = 4$	divide both sides by 1000

Darlene flew the plane for 4 hours.

❷ Using the Six Pretty Boxes approach:

	distance	rate	time
Darlene			t
Joe			

→

	distance	rate	time
Darlene			t
Joe			10 – t

	distance	rate	time
Darlene		600	t
Joe		400	10 – t

→

	distance	rate	time
Darlene	600t	600	t
Joe	400(10–t)	400	10 – t

9070. If four of the ten numbers are positive, and four of them are negative, then the remaining two numbers have to be zero. In a product of numbers if one (or more) of them is zero, then the final answer must be zero.

9073. $100^{1/2} = \sqrt{100} = 10$

The Complete Solutions and Answers

9081. The weight of Fred, a large size Stanthony combo pizza, and Darlene's nail polish collection are three consecutive numbers, when weighed in pounds. If you put Fred, the pizza, and Darlene's nail polish collection on a scale, they would weigh 111 pounds. How much does the pizza weigh?

First step: Let n = how much the pizza weighs. (You let the variable (n in this case) equal the thing you are trying to find out.)

Second step is writing the "Then . . ." statements:

Then $n - 1$ = equals Fred's weight.

Then $n + 1$ = the weight of Darlene's nail polish collection.

Since we know that the three things added together equal 111, we have:

$$n + (n - 1) + (n + 1) = 111$$

$$3n = 111$$

dividing both sides by 3 $n = 37$

The pizza weighs 37 pounds.

9087. The origin is the point (0, 0). For a graph to pass through the origin means that (0, 0) satisfies the equation.

Putting $x = 0$ and $y = 0$ into each of the equations:

$44x - 7y = 36$	becomes	$0 - 0 = 36$ which is false.
$200 = 30y$	becomes	$200 = 0$ which is false.
$5x = 88y$	becomes	$0 = 0$ which is true.

Only $5x = 88y$ passes through the origin.

9122. A trapezoid has an area of 980 square inches and the lengths of the parallel sides are 60 and 80 inches. What is the distance between the parallel sides?

The area formula for a trapezoid is $A = \frac{1}{2} h(a + b)$. Putting in the numbers that we know: $980 = \frac{1}{2} h(60 + 80)$.

$$980 = \frac{1}{2} h(140)$$

$$980 = 70h$$

$$14 = h \quad \text{dividing both sides by 70}$$

So the distance between the parallel sides is 14 inches.

9130. "{" and "}" are called braces.

The Complete Solutions and Answers

9225. Joe had to get from his apartment to a candy factory that is 148 miles away. He went in his old car at 60 mph and then it broke down, and he walked the rest of the way to the factory at 4 mph. He walked for 5 more hours than he drove. How long did he drive?

Note: I solve these word problems using two different approaches: ❶ the Let t = approach and the ❷ Six Pretty Boxes approach. You may choose either approach. They both work.

❶   Let t = the number of hours Joe drove. (We start word problems by letting the variable equal the thing we are trying to find out.)

Then t + 5 = the number of hours he walked. (He walked for 5 more hours than he drove. He drove for t hours.)

Then 60t = the miles he drove. (He drove at 60 mph for t hours.)

Then 4(t + 5) = the miles he walked. (He walked at 4 mph for t + 5 hours.)

Finally, since the sum of the miles he drove and the miles he walked was 148 miles, we have:

$$60t + 4(t + 5) = 148$$

Distributive law	$60t + 4t + 20 = 148$
Add	$64t + 20 = 148$
Subtract 20 from both sides	$64t = 128$
Divide both sides by 64	$t = 2$

Joe drove for 2 hours.

❷

	distance	rate	time
riding			t
walking			

→

	distance	rate	time
riding			t
walking			t + 5

←

	distance	rate	time
riding		60	t
walking		4	t + 5

→

	distance	rate	time
riding	60t	60	t
walking	4(t + 5)	4	t + 5

9230. { x | x = 2n where n is a whole number} is the set of all numbers that are twice any whole number. Since the whole numbers are {0, 1, 2, 3, 4, 5, . . . }, this set would be {0, 2, 4, 6, 8, . . . }.

9275. Without negative exponents, x^{-5} equals $\dfrac{1}{x^5}$

The Complete Solutions and Answers

9303. Darlene and Joe were standing outside of class. Joe said goodbye and headed north on his bicycle at the rate of 12 ft/sec. Sixty seconds later, Darlene decided to catch up with Joe. She headed north on her motor scooter at 15 ft/sec. How long will it take Darlene to catch up with Joe?

We will find the equation by using both methods: ❶ The "Let t = . . ." method; and ❷ by the Six Pretty Boxes method.

❶: Let t = the number of seconds it takes Darlene to catch up with Joe. (We always start by letting the variable equal the thing we want to find out.)

Then t + 60 = the number of seconds that Joe rode before Darlene caught up with him. (Since Joe rode 60 seconds longer than Darlene, and Darlene rode t seconds.)

Then 15t = the number of feet that Darlene rode. (Using d = rt and the facts that Darlene rode at 15 ft/sec for t seconds.)

Then 12(t + 60) = the number of feet that Joe rode. (Using d = rt and the facts that Joe rode at 12 ft/sec for t + 60 seconds.)

Finally, we have the equation 15t = 12(t + 60) (Since Darlene and Joe rode the same distance.)

Using the distributive law $15t = 12t + 720$
Subtract 12t from both sides $3t = 720$
Divide both sides by 3 $t = 240$

So Darlene rode for 240 seconds.

(For fun, let's check to make sure this is the correct answer. If Darlene rode for 240 seconds, then Joe must have ridden for 300 seconds. Darlene went 15×240 = 3600 feet. Joe went 12×300 = 3600 feet. They both went the same distance.)

❷: Using the Six Pretty Boxes approach.

	distance	r	t
Darlene			t
Joe			

→

	distance	r	t
Darlene			t
Joe			t + 60

↙

	distance	r	t
Darlene		15	t
Joe		12	t + 60

→

	distance	r	t
Darlene	15t	15	t
Joe	12(t+60)	12	t + 60

15t = 12(t + 60) and solve for t.

9306. $\dfrac{x^7 y^3}{x^2 y} = x^5 y^2$

Index

To learn about
other books
in this series
visit

FredGauss.com